D1205479

The

GLUYAS WILLIAMS

Gallery

Drawings

BY

Gluyas Williams

AND HIS *ILLUSTRATIONS*

WITH TEXT BY

Corey Ford

Edward Streeter

Laurence McKinney

David McCord

Robert Benchley

Ralf Kircher

The GLUYAS WILLIAMS *Gallery*

HARPER & BROTHERS PUBLISHERS

New York

THE GLUYAS WILLIAMS GALLERY

 FOR INFORMATION ADDRESS HARPER & BROTHERS, 49 EAST 33RD STREET, NEW YORK 16, N. Y. LIBRARY OF CONGRESS CATALOG CARD NUMBER: 57–8184.

Grateful acknowledgment is made to the following for permission to reprint selections included in this book:

DOUBLEDAY & COMPANY, INC. for *How to Guess Your Age* by Corey Ford, Copyright 1950 by Gluyas Williams, Copyright 1949, 1950 by Corey Ford; four chapters from *The Camp at Lockjaw* by David McCord, Copyright 1928 by Washburn & Thomas, Copyright 1952 by David McCord, Illustrations Copyright 1952 by Gluyas Williams.

E. P. DUTTON & CO., INC. for five poems from *People of Note* by Laurence McKinney, Copyright 1939, 1940 by Crowell-Collier Publishing Co., Copyright 1940 by Laurence McKinney.

HARPER & BROTHERS for selections from the following books by Robert Benchley: *After 1903—What?,* Copyright 1938 by Robert C. Benchley; *Chips Off the Old Benchley,* Copyright 1949 by Gertrude D. Benchley, Copyright 1933 by The Hearst Corporation; *The Early Worm,* Copyright 1927 by Harper & Brothers, Copyright 1955 by Gertrude D. Benchley; *From Bed to Worse,* Copyright 1934 by Robert C. Benchley; *My Ten Years in a Quandary,* Copyright 1936 by Robert C. Benchley; *No Poems,* Copyright 1932 by Robert Benchley; *Pluck and Luck,* Copyright 1925 by Harper & Brothers, Copyright 1953 by Gertrude D. Benchley; *20,000 Leagues Under the Sea,* Copyright 1928 by Harper & Brothers, Copyright 1956 by Gertrude D. Benchley.

The New Yorker Magazine: Of the 97 drawings in this collection, the 25 appearing on the following pages were published originally in *The New Yorker* and copyrighted in the respective years shown by The New Yorker Magazine, Inc.: pages 37, 78, 79 and 80, (1941); 38, 39, 40, 41 and 42, (1942); 190, 191, 193 and 194, (1944); 192, (1945); 94, 96 and 97, (1947); 95 and 98, (1948); 130, (1950); 127, 128 and 132, (1951); 129 and 131, (1953).

RINEHART & COMPANY, INC. for five chapters from *There's a Fly in This Room* by Ralf Kircher, Copyright 1946 by Ralf Kircher, and three chapters from *Wrap It as a Gift* by Ralf Kircher, Copyright 1947 by Ralf Kircher.

SIMON AND SCHUSTER, INC. for four chapters from *Father of the Bride* by Edward Streeter, Copyright 1948, 1949 by Edward Streeter and Gluyas Williams.

Contents

GLUYAS WILLIAMS THE MAN

by Edward Streeter

IN 1937 I decided to write a book on the horrors of commuting. The project presented only one difficulty. Quite obviously, the only artist capable of illustrating such a book was Gluyas Williams, and I couldn't conceive of his being interested in such a minor undertaking. In those days I did not know him personally but I finally screwed up my courage and proposed the idea to him one afternoon at the New York Harvard Club. To my amazement he agreed to do it without hesitation.

My lucky star was certainly hovering around that day, for not only did his incomparable drawings insure the success of *Daily Except Sundays* and a decade later of *Father of the Bride,* but our meeting was the beginning of a friendship which has definitely influenced my subsequent life and writing.

I am glad of the opportunity to acknowledge this debt. Prefaces, which are so seldom read, make excellent repositories for unvarnished truths, and the unvarnished truth in this instance is that Gluyas Williams is not only a great cartoonist but also a top-flight humorous writer. Fortunately for many of us he is so modest that this idea has never occurred to him. Had it done so he probably would have been illustrating his own books all these years and some of us would have found the going harder in consequence.

As I read over my file of his letters, written through the years, I realize how much I have absorbed of his style and point of view and how much I have profited from both.

It is futile to try to analyze anyone's special brand of humor—futile and risky, as it is apt to slide off the dissecting table and become lost, like the memory of a dream. Gluyas Williams' humor is a compound of gaiety and sadness, gallantry and failure, pompousness and frustration, mixed in accordance with some secret formula that he alone possesses and seasoned with a dash of futility and a pinch of wistfulness.

He sees humans as confused, insecure, well-intentioned duffers bluffing their way through a world of half-baked customs and screwball mores which they do not understand but cannot sidestep. You like his people and you sympathize with them for the good reason that they are always you—just as they are always Gluyas Williams.

He hates cant and pretension, but at the same time he is aware of the fact that, if one wants to roll down the normal, comfortable grooves of life (as most of us do), contact with a certain amount of both is unavoidable. With a few sparse strokes of his drawing pen he manages to convey the idea that his subjects are not only making fools of themselves, but are quite aware of it. One senses that, in spite of their embarrassment at being discovered, they will do nothing to correct the situation. They are caught in strong currents and find it easier to turn on their backs and float than to struggle against them.

This general atmosphere of genial hopelessness is an inherent part of the man as well as the artist. It crops out on almost every page of his revealing and always stimulating letters. I don't usually keep personal letters but for years I have stored Gluyas' away like a squirrel. He is almost the only person whom I know today who corresponds just for the joy of expressing himself and he is certainly the only one whose letters I have any desire to retain.

He almost always writes around Christmastime: fine, chatty, gloom-drenched epistles stuffed haphazardly with wit and wisdom. One of them starts, "Dear Ed: For some reason we woke up at four-thirty this morning and got up and had breakfast at five, which seemed like a sound idea at the time, but now at half-past seven I feel a little more than usually stupid and not at all ready to cope with the vast number of brilliant letters I had planned to dash off."

And on another similar occasion he is overcome by the knowledge of inevitable chaos. "If I am going to get a Christmas letter to you I had better start now because in a few days we are about to tear the house apart to get ready for the arrival of 1 son, 1 daughter, 1 daughter-in-law, 1 son-in-law and 4 grandchildren. My so-called studio has already been spoken for as a suitable place for the children to sleep and I think they can have a good time in it pouring bottles of India ink on the floors and going through my desk, scattering my income tax records."

Scattered through them are bits of deadpan humor and understatement that completely reflect the spirit of his drawings. I moved, and failed to give him my new address. "My last letter asking for your address went unanswered. Please let me know or I shall be forced to put my messages into a bottle and cast them into the sea which I feel is an old fashioned method of communication."

I admired his ability to type without hitting all the keys at the same time. "Learning to *type* as good as this is easy," he typed back. "I'll teach you if you'll teach me how to change the godam ribbon."

I complained of the daily extraneous details which had crept into my life since my retirement from business and which were preventing me from writing. "I'm not in the least surprised you've got yourself snarled up with booklets and committees and speeches. I'd have been agreeably surprised if you hadn't. But don't look forward to more leisurely days ahead. I've never been so busy as now when I've nothing to do. It takes so much longer to do it."

Humorists are supposed to be easygoing, rather slap-happy people, but no man ever set or maintained higher standards than Gluyas Williams in connection with creative work, whether it was his own or that of his friends.

Shortly after I met him, some twenty-odd years ago, he told me quite casually one day that he was giving up a lucrative advertising contract because it made him sick every time he worked on it. He spoke as if the incident was too trivial to need emphasis. Being a banker at the time, however, I looked on him as somewhat daft, for I knew that no comparable income from other sources was in hand. What I *didn't* know was Gluyas Williams.

In the summer of 1949 a well-known novelist spent a couple of days in my house in Chilmark, during the course of which I lured him into reading the manuscript of *Father of the Bride*. The only important suggestions he made were in connection with the first chapter, which because of my regard for his craftsmanship I immediately rewrote in accordance with his ideas. I sent the revision to Gluyas, who was then working on the drawings for the book. It came bouncing back accompanied by a letter which I regret to say has disappeared from my files. It berated me for taking anyone's advice about my own work, regardless of the fame or skill of the advisor. "You are creating something which is carved out of yourself," he said in effect. "Whether it is good or bad it must be *you.* If you let someone else push it around you can be sure it won't be *anybody.*" I put back the original version of the chapter.

Currently, Gluyas Williams is one of the most penetrating humorous artists of his time. At some future date, however, historians undoubtedly will turn to his drawings not for their humor but for what they reveal of the social customs and habits of an age that will then be gone, just as today scholars turn to Hogarth for the social history of eighteenth-century England. Perhaps this book, which brings together such a broad cross-section of Gluyas Williams' work, will be of help to them. I hope, however, for their sakes, that they will also be capable of appreciating the rich, human quality of these drawings which has caused their creator to be known and beloved by the civilized peoples of the world.

Somehow I think they will, for Gluyas Williams' work belongs to no one age.

GLUYAS WILLIAMS THE ARTIST

by David McCord

ONCE, in a moment of unaccountable inspiration, I wrote this sentence addressed to the graduating class of a small New England college: "Your life will be rich for others only as it is rich for you." It seems to me now that I must have been thinking of Gluyas Williams and his drawings in black and white. How rich, how variously rich for others is the great body of his work!

The paper on which I am writing these words is supported by the sheet of glass under which appears a view of the Lower Town of the city of Quebec as he drew it, with the great Château Frontenac and Dufferin Terrace soaring stupendous at the top. It is a winter day, and obviously ten or more below zero. In the foreground of the drawing appears a two-seated sleigh, the Christmas counterpart of the familiar *calèche*. In the driver's seat, the equally familiar Habitant himself, pointing with his whip toward some ancient landmark. Wrapped, robed, and scarfed, with a fur cap on his head, he looks aggressively snug and warm. Behind him, in the back seat, are Mr. and Mrs. Tourist with the remnants of a huge buffalo robe pulled up to their double chins. They are obviously half frozen. A dozen adults and children quietly animate the narrow sidewalks. A second sleigh, with additional congealed occupants, is disappearing at an intersection toward the river. The view, I am certain, is of *Côte de la Montagne;* and the three youngsters looking in at the lighted window of a little shop in the curving middle background are standing just about where I stood long ago as a very small boy, while my father explained to me the first word in French which I had ever overheard. It was *lapin*: rabbit. Dear God! One crystal moment of my youth comes back to me whenever I look at this drawing from across my desk: enormous simplification against a background of intricate and charming detail; the quiet humor of contrast so deceptively achieved with cool, unstudied grace.

This universal human quality—a love, not a contempt, for his fellow man—is what sets Gluyas Williams in a class by himself. Satire has no place in his method of characterization. Even his painfully correct reporting of some of America's incredible playgrounds shows not the slightest trace of mockery. That crowds of men and women can look and act as they do, and affect to find pleasure and recreation in the sordid mass, is part of the subdivine comedy into which he enters as a spectator, never as a critic. Not long ago I visited a somewhat lonely little lake in New Hampshire for the opening day of trout and landlocked salmon fishing. When dawn broke there appeared over the water a miraculous blue haze which I did not remember having seen either in the wilderness of southern Oregon where I grew up or in Canada where I have often fished. Ten minutes later I discovered that this came from the exhaust of dozens of outboard engines racing their boatloads of fishermen to fancied stations over superior fish. The bedlam was unbelievable. It discouraged me beyond hope; but to Gluyas it would have appeared as a miracle of humor, and he would have sorted out and remembered the pathetic and the grotesque, and the tangling of tackle near the shore, to bring the whole scene into focus: incredible, fantastic, but absolutely human, and uncontrollably American.

How has he achieved this skill? Like Robert Frost, he has always been an artist with a single purpose. For Frost it is poetry alone; for Gluyas Williams it has been drawing solely in black and white. When did he begin? Well, W. H. Hudson was once asked how long he had been married. "As long as I can remember," he said—which is exactly how long the subject of this book has been at work with pen and pencil. While in college—only three years to the A.B.—he was an art editor of the Harvard *Lampoon*. Then he went to Paris for a year, drew from life in Colarossi's studio, returned to Boston and drew first for the old Boston *Journal* and second for the dearly remembered Boston *Evening Transcript;* and finally appeared in *Life,* largely under the editorship of Charles Dana Gibson. When *Life* had its face lifted along in 1930, Gluyas moved into *The New Yorker* as easily as an eagle flies home to its eyrie. Later, of course, there were also Fred Perley and his fellow characters in the newspaper syndicated drawings. As to that, I much lament the fact that there is no Fred Perley in this book.

Of the Master's connection with the *Transcript*—always hospitable to young talent: Gilbert Seldes, Kenneth Macgowan, Brooks Atkinson, and John Mason Brown, for example—Forrest Izard has written this:

> For some years in the second decade of the century, Gluyas often made charming drawings of theatrical folk for the Boston *Evening Transcript*. . . . My chore was to write a sort of pseudo-Arabian-Night account of the evening; Gluyas did half a dozen drawings. The extraordinary thing was that during all the extremely busy back-stage-goings-on, Gluyas never made a sketch. He just looked and looked—and remembered. The pictures, printed a few days later, were a total recall: costumes, characters, and situations all were there.

The art of drawing in black and white without wash or shading—Mr. Williams *occasionally* indulges in Ben Day—is diabolically difficult. There is no short cut to suggesting mystery, and absolutely nothing of the surprise produced so often in the well-controlled accident of water color. Every figure in a Williams drawing is doing something of value to the picture; every niche and quarter of the background is justified and correct. The illusion of distance, rain, and atmosphere, and of the unexplained, is effected solely by "the lucid, faultless line we have come so to admire." In speaking of that, Mr. Matlack Price (*American Artist,* April, 1948) observes that Mr. Williams has never used Chinese white because Aubrey Beardsley was supposed not to use it. It was something of a shock, therefore, when the young American discovered some Beardsleys "fairly plastered with Chinese white."

But remarkable as remains that lucid line, and the Williams sense of composition, I would not underemphasize the unerring disposal of those solid accents: the vest, the tie, the mustache, the hatband, the bald man's fringe of hair, the black umbrella, the pair of shorts. These black areas, since they stand out first, he puts in last.

Kenneth Bird, sometime editor of *Punch,* and known to the literate world by his superlative drawings signed Fougasse, has called Gluyas Williams "a superb noticer." What Mr. Bird said about his American contemporary, quoted at some length by William Webb in the *Christian Science Monitor* of January 6, 1951, is worth mention. "It will be readily agreed," he writes, "that Gluyas is in a class by himself; but to put this down to his drawing, or to his technique. or to the style that he adopted would be to do him very much less than justice."

I have been talking in the main about those drawings which stand entirely by themselves. Each of us has a favorite. For myself, I think of what the woman said to the Philosopher in *The Crock of Gold*: "I like one as well as the other and better, and I'd as soon have one as the other and rather."

Of his illustrations for many books by various authors, I venture but this word: All of us who have written things, which Gluyas was willing to illustrate, openly agree that we were both fortunate and privileged. This is his book, not ours. If we have ever let him down, he has always held us up. If any character in print exhibited a vitamin deficiency, Gluyas restored him to health. He is a wise doctor as well as a great artist.

I began these words with a reference to Canada. Without his permission, I quote from a letter which Gluyas wrote me early in 1955: "When my Canadian grandson visited us as a two-year-old, and was taken to church, he stood on the pew, surveyed the congregation and remarked, 'Nice party, eh?' "

That is the way I feel about this book.

I.

How to Guess Your Age

By COREY FORD

It seems to me that they are building staircases steeper than they used to. The risers are higher, or there are more of them, or something.

Maybe this is because it is so much farther today from the first floor to the second floor, but I've noticed it is getting harder to make two steps at a time any more. Nowadays it is all I can do to make one step at a time.

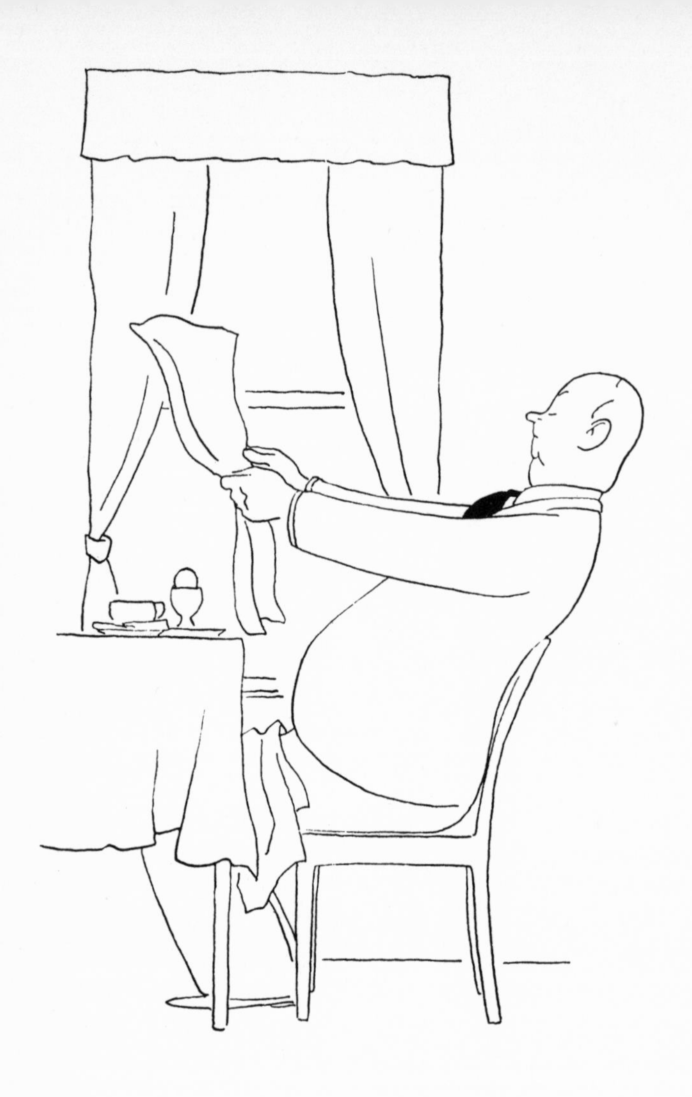

Another thing I've noticed is the small print they're using lately. Newspapers are getting farther and farther away when I hold them, and I have to squint to make them out.

The other day I had to back halfway out of a telephone booth in order to read the number on the coin box. It is obviously ridiculous to suggest that a person my age needs glasses, but the only other way I can find out what's going on is to have somebody read aloud to me, and that's not too satisfactory because people speak in such low voices these days that I can't hear them very well.

Everything is farther than it used to be. It's twice the distance from my house to the station now, and they've added a fair-sized hill that I never noticed before.

The trains leave sooner too. I've given up running for them, because they start faster these days when I try to catch them.

You can't depend on timetables any more, and it's no use asking the conductor. I ask him a dozen times a trip if the next station is where I get off, and he always says it isn't. How can you trust a conductor like that?

Usually I gather up my bundles and put on my hat and coat and stand in the aisle a couple of stops away, just to make sure I don't go past my destination. Sometimes I make doubly sure by getting off at the station ahead.

A lot of other things are different lately. Barbers no longer hold up a mirror behind me when they've finished, so I can see the back of my head, and my wife has been taking care of the tickets lately when we go to the theater.

They don't use the same material in clothes any more, either. I've noticed that all my suits have a tendency to shrink, especially in certain places such as around the waist or in the seat of the pants, and

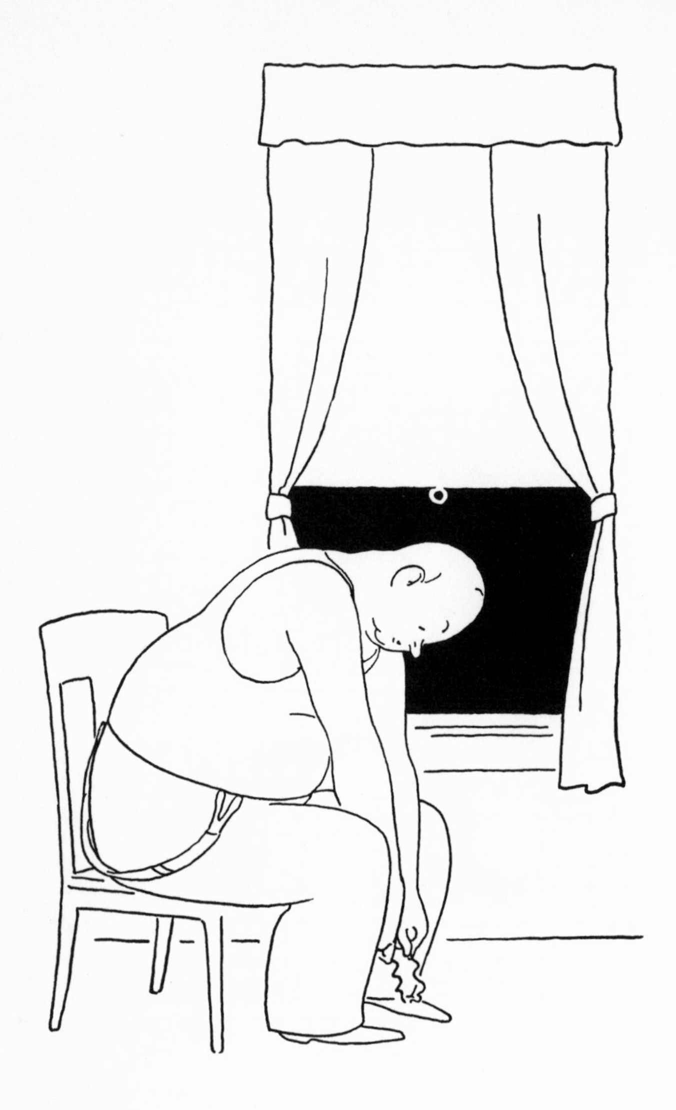

the laces they put in shoes nowadays are harder to reach.

Revolving doors revolve much faster than they used to. I have to let a couple of openings go past me before I jump in, and by the time I get up nerve enough to jump out again I'm right back in the street where I started. It's the same with golf. I'm giving it up because these modern golf balls they sell are so hard to pick up when I stoop over. I've had to quit driving, too; the restrooms in filling

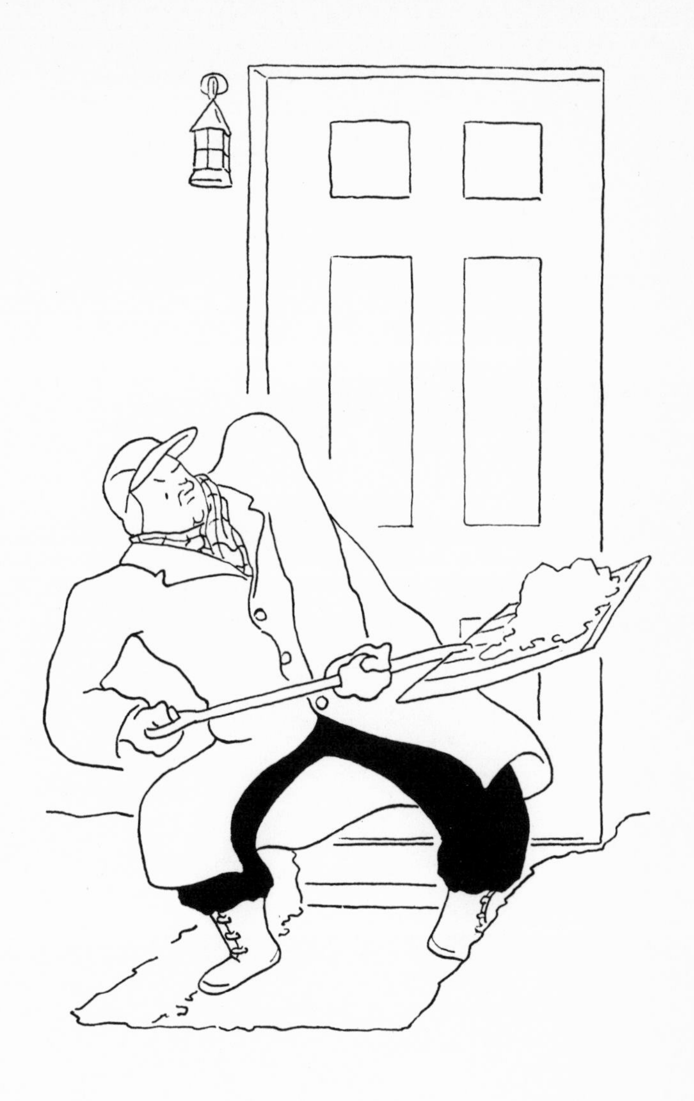

stations are getting farther and farther apart. Usually I just stay home at night and read the papers, particularly the obituary columns. It's funny how much more interesting the obituary columns have been getting lately.

Even the weather is changing. It's colder in winter, and the summers are hotter than they used to be. I'd go away, if it wasn't so far. Snow is heavier when I try to shovel it, and I have to put on rub-

bers whenever I go out, because rain today is wetter than the rain we used to get. Draughts are more severe too. It must be the way they build windows now.

People are changing too. For one thing, they're younger than they used to be when I was their age. I went back recently to an alumni reunion at the college I graduated from in 1943—that is, 1933—I mean, 1923—and I was shocked to see the mere

tots they're admitting as students these days. The average age of the freshman class couldn't have been more than seven. They seem to be more polite than in my time, though; several undergraduates

called me "Sir," and one of them asked me if he could help me across the street.

On the other hand, people my own age are so much older than I am. I realize that my generation is approaching middle age (I define middle age roughly as the period between 21 and 110) but there is no excuse for my classmates tottering into a state of advanced senility. I ran into my old roommate at the bar, and he'd changed so much that he didn't recognize me. "You've put on a little weight, George," I said.

"It's this modern food," George said. "It seems to be more fattening."

"How about another martini?" I said. "Have you noticed how much weaker the martinis are these days?"

"Everything is different," said George. "Even the food you get. It's more fattening."

"How long since I've seen you, George?" I said. "It must be several years."

"I think the last time was right after the election," said George.

"What election was that?"

George thought for a moment. "Harding."

I ordered a couple more martinis. "Have you noticed these martinis are weaker than they used to be?" I said.

"It isn't like the good old days," George said. "Remember when we'd go down to the speak, and order some Orange Blossoms, and maybe pick up a couple of flappers? Boy, could they neck! Hot diggety!"

"You used to be quite a cake-eater, George," I said. "Do you still do the Black Bottom?"

"I put on too much weight," said George. "This food nowadays seems to be more fattening."

"I know," I said, "you mentioned that just a minute ago."

"Did I?" said George.

"How about another martini?" I said. "Have

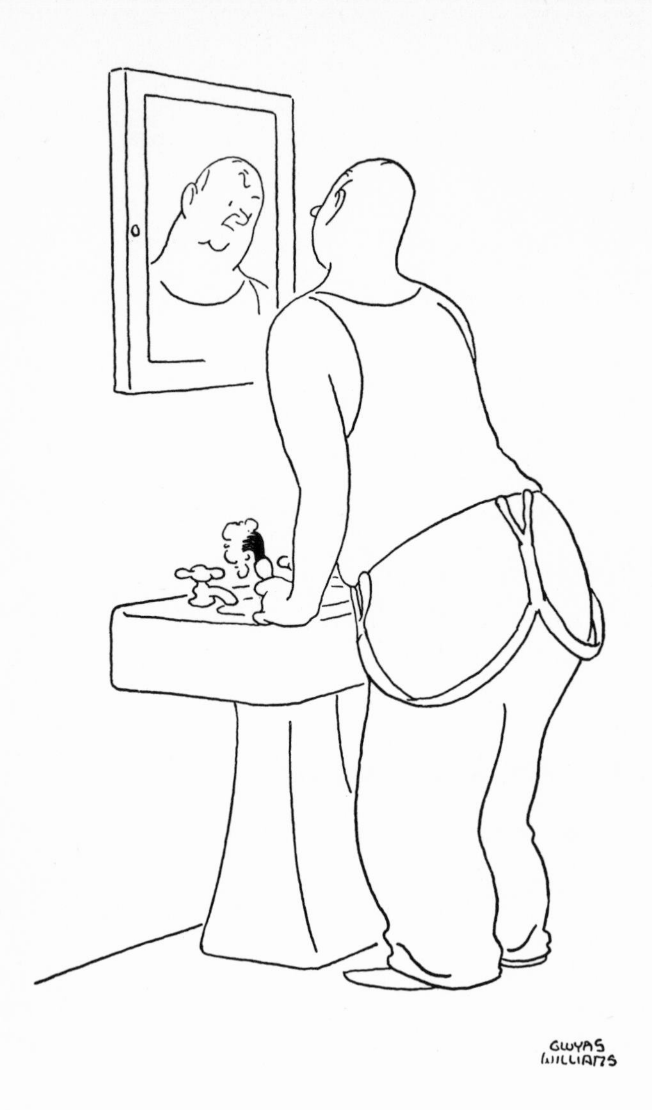

you noticed the martinis aren't as strong as the
used to be?"

"Yes," said George, "you said that twice before.

"Oh," I said. . . .

I got to thinking about poor old George while
was shaving this morning, and I stopped for a mo
ment and looked at my own reflection in the mirro

They don't seem to use the same kind of glass i
mirrors any more.

II.

The Reading Public

By GLUYAS WILLIAMS

With Captions by Russell Maloney

"Another case finished, another poor, misguided vil who will pay for his crimes on the gallows." spector Trunnel leaned back comfortably, crossed s tweed-clad legs, and dipped his pipe into his bacco pouch.

"I'm afraid I'm most awfully dense, but I still n't see how you worked it out," I said, pushing e decanter toward him. "Why, I thought Gruber d the best alibi of the whole lot."

"That's just it, my boy," said Trunnel. "He had too good an alibi. Mark you, Sheila Trent-Quayle said she saw him in the yew alley before ten forty-three, when she retired. Of course, we now know that she was covering up for young Lovering, who she feared was implicated. But if Gruber didn't go to the stables before eleven-three, and if the butler didn't set out the tray of sandwiches until eleven-fifteen, that scene in the billiard room between Gruber and Blaylock couldn't have taken place before midnight. Here, let me just draw up a timetable . . ."

Mitzi Sweezey will not wed Randall Trotter III, as rumored in that column. Her heart is a G-man, and he still carries the torch for Lulu LaFlamme, Dotty Club eyeful . . . The wise money is betting that a certain local biggie will be offered a certain federal job. Watch and see if we aren't right . . . Ironical how horses bob up in the life of Joe Turley, popular emsee. Joe got his start as a chorus boy in the musical "Whoa, Dobbin!" Four years ago almost won the daily double at Empire City. N comes word that Peggy Giffins, his ex-flame, is of the floor show at El Trocador due to a bite fr a policeman's mount. And—here's the payeroo— can't ride a horse . . . heheheh . . . Broadway— street where the rats steal cheese out of each oth traps . . . Hitler is secretly planning a . . .

'he view of the sunrise from midstream was an 'orgettable experience, with the sun coming up m behind the famous old castles of the Rhine ' casting great shadows on the water. The "inner n" was calling, however, and it was a welcome ef when our little Folbot caravan "dropped anchor" at the little hamlet of Umbrau, where we unslung knapsacks, washed up, and breakfasted cozily in the taproom of the historic old inn. We were told by the innkeeper, a bearded patriarch whose picture we snapped (page 97), that a side trip to the picturesque forest of Ubergrau would repay . . .

"Stock Broker" may be played by two to seven players. If more than three or less than five play, the scoring is based on the total number of points lost when the winner "goes off;" otherwise the winning score is One Hundred and Fifty-five.

Each player is given three dice, $1,500 in "play money," six forfeit cards (which, before the game begins, he may exchange with those drawn by his left-hand neighbor, who then must redeem them from the Bank), and two penalty cards, which remain face down.

Each player rolls his three dice until one shoots a double six and a three. This makes him Banker for that round (unless he draws a forfeit card, wh makes the Bank forfeit to the lowest bidder) a the player at his left is the Dealer. (Any player the lowest hand may "challenge" either the Dea or the Banker, or both, by drawing a penalty c entitling him to "auction off" the Bank or the D to the lowest bidder.)

The Banker starts the game by "asking for posits." If no one chooses to deposit (or if no is able to, because of unfavorable forfeit cards), Banker may then "call for more margin" from player at his right, who then has the choice of " ing for a mortgage," "freezing his assets," or .

. . . and now the Prince enters the glade, seeking the wounded deer. The Princess and her handmaidens flee in alarm. The Prince executes a pas de deux with the Spirit of the Glade, and then disappears into the depths of the forest, pressing his search for the deer. The deer enters, fleeing from the Prince. The Princess and her handmaidens return, hiding from the Grand Vizier, and the deer, alarmed . . .

For the purpose of this discussion, it is desirable to separate the purely logical concept of being *from the actual* fact of existence—*without, of course, forgetting that the two are related through the* will to be, *which manifests itself in the subrational* act of willing. *Thus we avoid the pitfall presented by the confusion of* I will *with* I am, *though, to be sur another danger lurks in the negation of* I am *throug the purely pragmatic concept of the* will-to-be *part of the* will-be. *Note, however (Appendix I pp. 439–467), that Grüssboscher proceeds on t assumption, erroneous in our opinion, that . . .*

III.

FROM

Father of the Bride

By EDWARD STREETER

Getting Acquainted

BUCKLEY, Kay informed her parents with her best Old School irony, *also* had a father and mother. It seemed to her that the situation called for a minimum display of interest from the Banks family unless, of course, they preferred to make it look like a shotgun wedding and introduce themselves at the altar rail.

Mr. Banks agreed moodily. The obvious fact that he must do something about meeting Buckley's family had been weighing on him for some time. Although he had never considered himself a shy man, the idea gave him as much pleasure as a summons to appear before a congressional committee. He had been postponing action from day to day in the same way that he put off wearing a pair of new shoes to the office.

"I suppose Kay's right," he admitted gloomily to Mrs. Banks. "We've got to face it."

"I don't understand why you get in such a lather about it," she said. "What's so awful about meeting Buckley's father and mother?"

"Who said I was in a lather?" he retorted sharply. "All I mean is you'd think Kay might have picked out somebody we knew instead of a family we never laid eyes on and that are probably God-awful. I just know the kind of people they are. It's going to be terrible."

"Stanley Banks, for a grown man you sometimes don't make any sense. In the first place I don't see why you assume the Dunstans are terrible and in the second you're not marrying Buckley's family."

"I might just as well be," groaned Mr. Banks. "I'll probably have to support them."

The Dunstans eventually took matters into their own hands and invited Mr. and Mrs. Banks to East Smithfield for Sunday dinner; just the four of them—without Kay and Buckley—so they could get acquainted.

"That's the pay-off," said Mr. Banks. "They're the cozy type."

He made no further comment, but during the intervening days he showed all the symptoms of a debutante about to be introduced at Buckingham Palace. On Sunday morning he dressed carefully in a sport coat and slacks, then went upstairs after breakfast and changed into a business suit. He insisted on starting half an hour earlier than was necessary—just to allow for a blowout or something. The result was that they arrived in East Smithfield shortly after twelve.

Mr. Banks said he'd be damned if he was going to sit and moon at the Dunstans' for an hour. He preferred to slum around the town and get a line on the natives.

"I'll bet they won't even have a drink before dinner," he said gloomily.

"How do you know they won't?"

"Because I know. That's the kind of people they are."

"Well, suppose they don't. You're not an alcoholic, are you?"

Mr. Banks sighed but didn't pursue the argument.

"I think it might be more intelligent to find out where the Dunstans live instead of driving around aimlessly," said Mrs. Banks. "At least we won't end up by being late."

"I'll bet it's a shack," said Mr. Banks.

When they finally located it, the Dunstan shack turned out to be a large, whitewashed brick house about a mile out of town. It sat well back from the road surrounded by old elm trees. The discovery that it was at least twice the size of his own seemed to add fuel to Mr. Banks' agitation. He looked at his watch.

"I'm going back to that hotel we passed and wash up," he announced.

"Nonsense," said Mrs. Banks. "You can wash at the Dunstans'. They probably have running water."

"I prefer to wash at the hotel," said Mr. Banks with dignity. She sensed that this was not the time to cross him.

When they drew up in front of the hotel he did not suggest that she get out, but hurried through the revolving doors. On his return, ten minutes later, it was obvious that he was more composed. The interior of the sedan immediately took on the Saturday night odor of a bar-and-grill.

"Stanley Banks, you've been drinking."

Mr. Banks did not take his eyes off the road ahead. "Why is it," he asked, "that a person can't take a casual drink without being accused of 'drinking'? It does seem to me that a man over fifty—"

"I think it's perfectly outrageous for you to meet the Dunstans smell-

The fact that it was about twice the size of his own establishment seemed to add fuel to his agitation.

ing like an old whiskey bottle. It's humiliating, that's what it is. What in the world's gotten into you? And Sunday morning, too."

"What's Sunday morning got to do with it?" asked Mr. Banks, hoping to divert the argument. But Mrs. Banks was still being difficult when they turned in at the Dunstans' entrance.

The first meeting of in-laws is comparable to the original hookup of the Lewis and Clark Expedition with the Rocky Mountain Indians.

In the latter instance it is recorded that for a brief moment after the encounter both sides glared at one another with mingled hostility and curiosity. At this point a false move would have been fatal. If anyone had so much as reached for his tobacco pouch the famous Journals would never have seen the light of day.

Then, each side finding the other apparently unarmed, the tension eased. The leaders stepped forward, embraced, rubbed noses and muttered "How." Skins were spread and refreshments laid on them by squaws. The party was in the bag.

The Banks-Dunstan meeting followed similar lines. For a split second the two families stared at one another in the Dunstan entrance hall. During that instant Mrs. Banks took inventory of Mrs. Dunstan from hair-do to shoes. Mrs. Dunstan did the same for Mrs. Banks. Then, finding everything mutually satisfactory, they approached one another with outstretched arms, embraced and said, "My dear."

The two males merely shook hands awkwardly and said in unison, "It certainly is nice to meet you."

Mrs. Dunstan started to lead the way into the living room. "Would you like to wash your hands?" asked Mr. Dunstan.

"I've washed them," said Mr. Banks, glancing at him suspiciously.

"I can't tell you how crazy we are about your Kay," said Mrs. Dunstan.

"Well, that's just the way we feel about Buckley," said Mrs. Banks.

"Yes indeed," said Mr. Banks. Obviously something was called for.

As far as he was concerned that seemed about all there was to be said. He would have been quite ready to second a motion to adjourn.

The situation was saved by the appearance of a maid with a shaker full of martinis and a tray of hot hors d'oeuvres. Mr. Banks looked at this arrangement with pleased incredulity.

He took a martini and found it excellent. "I think we should drink

For a split second the two families stared at one another.

to the bride and groom," said Mr. Dunstan. Mr. Banks drank deeply and relaxed like a deflating balloon. Mr. Dunstan refilled the glasses.

Warmed by this unexpected hospitality and his previous wash-up at the hotel, Mr. Banks felt impelled to words. "This is an important occasion," he said. "My wife and I have been looking forward to it for a long time. Personally I thought your son was a great fellow the moment I set eyes on him. Now that I've met his father and mother I like him even better. From here in I foresee that the Dunstan-Banks families will beat as one."

"I am sure we're going to be most congenial," said Mrs. Dunstan apprehensively, "and do call us Doris and Herbert, not Mr. and Mrs. Dunstan."

"And Stanley and Ellie," said Mrs. Banks somewhat overeagerly.

There was an embarrassed silence.

"Have you ever been in Fairview Manor, Herbert?" asked Mr. Banks.

"No, we haven't, Stanley. We've heard a lot about it, of course."

"I love your house, Doris," said Mrs. Banks, who had by this time sized up and appraised critically every article of furniture in the living room.

"Thank you, Ellie. We like it. I'm crazy to see yours. Buckley's always talking about it."

"Another, Stan?" asked Mr. Dunstan.

"Well, just to help you out, Herb," said Mr. Banks.

His wife moved over beside him. "You'd better watch your step," she muttered.

It was too late. The release from supertension was more than he could combat. He graciously helped his friend Herb finish up the shaker.

"I think dinner is ready," said Mrs. Dunstan, who had known it for a long time.

She led the way toward the dining room. "You've got a wonderful place here, Edith," said Mr. Banks, falling in beside her.

"Doris," she said. "Won't you sit there, Ellie. And now we want to hear all about our new daughter."

"I'm afraid there isn't much to tell," said Mrs. Banks.

"Nonsense," said Mr. Banks. "Would you like to hear the story about how Ellie left Kay in her baby carriage outside the A. & P. and then forgot about her and went home?"

He told them in hilarious detail. A flood of memories and anecdotes

He graciously helped his friend Herb finish up the shaker.

poured from him like a mountain brook. He took them through Kay's childhood and school days step by step. Then, as a kind of appendix, he gave them a detailed account of his own boyhood, early manhood and married life. Occasionally one of the Dunstans broke in with a comment. Toward the end of the meal they ceased to compete.

After dinner Mr. Banks picked out a comfortable-looking chair in the darkest corner of the living room. He felt suddenly drowsy. "Now," he said, "you must tell us all about Buckley." The desire to take just forty winks became overpowering. As Buckley entered his first year in high school Mr. Banks' eyes closed and he was instantly asleep.

They drove back to Fairview Manor late in the afternoon, Mrs. Banks at the controls. Mr. Banks felt relaxed and happy. It was hard for him to understand why he had dreaded this meeting so much. He sought in vain among his acquaintances for a finer family than the Dunstans. Certainly no one could have been easier to talk to. He hummed a contented little song. Mrs. Banks said nothing.

Financial Matters

IT WAS quite clear to Mr. Banks that things couldn't drift along like this forever. When two people decided to get married they announced their engagement and then there was a wedding. The only question was when.

As his mind focused on the actual ceremony he began to have secret qualms about it. Weddings had never meant much to him one way or the other. They were pleasant parties where he was apt to run into a lot of people whom he had not seen lately. Now, when he considered his role as father of the bride, it became alarmingly apparent that he was slated to play a lead part in what looked more and more to him like a public spectacle. Unconsciously he was experiencing the first symptoms of aisle-shyness.

When it came to discussing the date, therefore, he was like a man who has rashly committed himself to go swimming in a glacial stream. His idea was either to get the affair over as quickly as possible or else postpone it to a point so far distant in time that, like death, he wouldn't have to worry about it for the present at least.

Mrs. Banks, on the other hand, looked at the matter more from the point of view of a stage manager. How long would it take to prepare the costumes, build the scenery and collect the props? She concluded that, working day and night, the production might be staged in three months—not a minute earlier.

During the discussions that followed Buckley remained unusually silent. He was obviously a young man who was not used to getting married and these unfolding and complex plans seemed to bewilder him. As he listened to his future mother-in-law he became gradually panic-stricken. He explained to her with desperate finality that he was a simple fellow who wanted no trappings or lugs. His idea of a wedding was a little ivy-covered chapel in some lovely country spot where he and Kay could walk down the aisle hand in hand.

He watched with dismay as the storm raged around him.

Mr. Banks decided to switch the conversation into lighter vein. Buckley was inclined to have a heavy touch at moments. He said that was a fine idea. He liked it. The trouble was that the only kind of ivy that grew around Fairview Manor was poisonous and the only place that approximated a lovely country spot was the golf course.

Kay interrupted. This was scarcely the time for cheap comedy. And besides, everyone seemed to have forgotten an important point. This was *her* wedding. *She* was the one who was getting married—not Pops or Mom. Buckley of course—but it was *her* wedding nonetheless and she didn't propose to be pushed around by *anybody*. She would marry *when* and *where* the spirit moved her. Perhaps it would be in two weeks, perhaps in six *months*.

What was more, there was no need for all this fussing. Her mother didn't need to raise a *hand*—not a finger. When she (Kay) gave the word everything would fall into place. That was the way she and Buckley were going to live. Simply and without all this *effort*. She had seen *nothing* but fuss and feathers all her life. Now she wanted no more of it. That might as well be understood.

From this point on the conversation began to resemble the Chicago wheat pit on the day of a big break. It was Buckley's first family free-for-all. Quite obviously it upset him. From where he sat, in a corner of the living room, it seemed like the breakup of basic relationships. He watched with dismay as the storm raged. Then, like a tropical hurricane, it was unexpectedly over. Instead of the tangled and broken wreckage which he had anticipated, he was astonished to learn that it had been harmoniously agreed that the wedding would take place on Friday, June 10, at four-thirty P.M. at St. George's Church.

"Are you awake?" asked Mr. Banks. "Hey, Ellie."

Mrs. Banks stirred uneasily.

"Are you awake?"

"What's the matter?" she asked, noncommittally, regarding him with one unfriendly eye.

"I've been thinking," said Mr. Banks. "I've been thinking all night. I haven't slept."

"You were snoring when I woke up," she said, without sympathy.

Mr. Banks ignored the remark. It was merely part of Mrs. Banks' morning routine.

"I've been thinking about Buckley," he said. "I'm worried. Good and worried. Do you realize, Ellie, that we know next to nothing about this boy? Just because his family has a big house and a couple of maids doesn't mean anything. What do we know about *him*?"

He raised himself on his elbow. "Think it over a minute. One day Kay comes home and says, 'This is Buckley. Isn't he cute? I'm going to marry him.' And we all make faces at him and dance around. But what do we *know* about him?"

Mr. Banks began to check off his points on his fingers. "Has he got any money? You don't know. What's he making? Nobody knows. Can he support her? We just don't know a darn thing about the guy. He walks in the door and we hand him Kay and—"

"Darling," interrupted Mrs. Banks, "we've been through all this before. Ask Buckley. Don't ask me."

"Don't try to laugh it off." Mr. Banks was working himself into one of his pre-breakfast frenzies. *"I'm* not going to support him. Not by a damn sight. I'm—"

Mrs. Banks interrupted again. "Listen, dear. I think you're absolutely right. I've told you so every time you've brought this up. We should have found out about these things long ago. I don't know why you haven't. You've been going to have a talk with Buckley ever since Kay first told us. Sometimes I think you're a little afraid of him."

Mr. Banks snorted. "That's a fine remark, I must say. I intend to have a talk with him, all right. We might just as well have it out."

He sat on the edge of his bed radiating aggressiveness. Mrs. Banks thought he looked rather gray and tired.

By the time he reached home that evening he had decided not to make a direct approach. No use scaring the boy to death. Instead he told Kay that he wanted to have a little talk with Buckley about finances. You know—what he was earning and all that sort of thing. As a sop to liberalism he indicated that he thought Buckley was entitled to know something about *his* affairs.

Kay accepted this with irritating patience. She said O.K. if that was what he wanted. Buckley was big enough to take it. *She* knew what he was making and that should be all that was necessary, *but* if Pops wanted to go into all that old-fashioned rigamarole—O.K. She'd give Buckley the message.

Several nights later Buckley arrived for dinner carrying a bulging briefcase. Mr. Banks eyed it dubiously. What did the fellow think he was—a C.P.A.? On the other hand, if he had enough papers to fill that thing, the picture might not be as grim as he had feared. Rather decent of the boy to take it so seriously.

Mr. Banks had visualized a quiet, dignified conversation during which he would be seated in a large armchair and Buckley in a straight chair facing him. Instead he found himself sitting beside Buckley on the living-room sofa making old-fashioneds.

He finished his quickly. Somehow he felt the need of fortification. After a while Ben and Tommy drifted off on their own affairs and a few minutes later Mrs. Banks and Kay disappeared in the direction of the kitchen. It was Delilah's night out. Mr. Banks was glad of this. Buckley would see that they were a quiet, simple family, well able to take care of itself, but not equipped to assume extra burdens.

They were alone. The time had come. Mixing himself another old-fashioned, he plunged.

"I guess Kay has told you," he said, "that I wanted to have a little financial chat with you." He thought this rather a footless opening in view of the briefcase resting at Buckley's feet.

"Yes, sir," said Buckley, reaching for the briefcase.

Mr. Banks raised a delaying hand. "In the old days," he continued, "fathers used to say to prospective sons-in-law, 'Are you going to be able to support my daughter in the manner to which she's accustomed?' " Unintentionally he gave a throaty laugh. Buckley did not even smile.

"I know what you kids are up against, though, and I've got modern ideas about these things." He stopped himself from adding, "although I may not look it."

Buckley nodded understandingly. He reminded Mr. Banks more and more of a family doctor paying a professional visit.

"What I mean is I know what you young people are up against. You all need help and I believe parents should give it as far as they are able."

"Yes, sir," agreed Buckley.

"What I was going on to say," continued Mr. Banks hurriedly, "is that parents are also up against it these days."

"They certainly are," said Buckley.

"You know what I mean—with high taxes and high prices and one thing and another."

Buckley nodded sympathetically.

"The long and the short of it is I think you're just as entitled to know where I stand as I am to know about you."

"Yes, sir," said Buckley, reaching for his briefcase.

Buckley continued to regard him like a family doctor.

Mr. Banks hurried on. "So here's what I propose. I'll start out and tell you a little about my own setup. You and Kay ought to know just how much you can count on us for help in the pinches—and just how much you can't. Then you can go into your financial picture. How about it, eh?"

Buckley continued to regard him gravely.

"What I mean is, we ought to know about each other," added Mr. Banks.

"Yes, sir," said Buckley.

Mr. Banks took a thoughtful drink. "I've often wished my father-in-law had sat down with me before Kay's mother and I were married and told me more about himself. Young people are so apt to take things for granted and expect things that aren't possible."

"That's right," said Buckley.

Mr. Banks glanced at him quickly, but Buckley was fumbling with the catch on his briefcase.

"Well, to begin with—" said Mr. Banks nervously.

At the end of fifteen minutes Buckley knew more about Mr. Banks' affairs than Mrs. Banks had been able to dig out in a lifetime. He listened with grave attention and nodded understandingly from time to time. Mr. Banks' feeling that he was consulting his doctor became stronger as he went on. When he had finished if Buckley had pulled a stethoscope out of his briefcase and asked him to strip to the waist he would have complied without question. Instead Buckley removed a large sheaf of papers from the briefcase.

"I've brought some papers," he said, somewhat unnecessarily.

"Soup's on," cried Mrs. Banks from the living-room door, in her gayest company manner. "My, you two look solemn. Come now or it will get cold."

"That's all right, my boy. We'll do your side later."

Kay jumped up from the table before they had finished dessert. "Come on, Buckley, we're late. Sorry, Mom, we promised to meet the Bakers and go to the movies. Pops kept Buckley talking too long. You don't mind if we skip the dishes do you?"

"Of course not, dear. Run along."

"Did you have a good talk with Buckley?" she asked as they cleared the dining-room table.

"Very satisfactory," said Mr. Banks moodily.

These Shall Be the Wedding Guests

YOU PEOPLE are looking at this whole thing upside down," said Mr. Banks. "It's not a question of how many people you *want*. You must start with the *house*. How many can stand in it at one time? The extras get jammed into the church."

After tense debate it was decided that one hundred and fifty was the absolute maximum that could be packed into 24 Maple Drive without physical injury. An additional one hundred might receive invitations to the church, but certainly not to the reception.

This did not mean, of course, that the invitations must be limited to these numbers. People living at great distances wouldn't show up if they were in their right minds, so the Bankses might as well get the credit for having asked them. Then, with any luck at all, it was safe to count on a certain number of local people being sick, or out of town, on the day of the wedding.

Mr. Banks estimated that they could rely on refusals from a third of the local invitations. On that basis, and excluding the out-of-towners, they could ask two hundred and twenty-five to both the church and the reception and one hundred and fifty additional just to the church.

To Mrs. Banks, who was used to entertaining on a retail level, this seemed like a staggering number. She proposed that each one make a separate list—just the people they *really* wanted. Then these could be combined, the duplicates eliminated—and there you were. If there were more than two hundred and twenty-five, which was unlikely, the excess could be asked to the church only.

This task occupied an harmonious evening.

Mrs. Banks jotted down the names of all living relatives (and her memory was encyclopedic), plus her special cronies in the Garden and Bridge Clubs; also all the people who had invited Mr. Banks and herself to dinner in the last few years—and whom she had neglected to ask back.

Kay put down the classmates who had written fatuous messages across her photograph in her copy of the Heathwood Hall class album, all the young men who had ever asked her to major football games, and people whom she had visited for more than two days. In a burst of gratitude she threw in the fathers and mothers of those who had put her up (or vice versa) for more than a week. To these were added her former cronies at the Fairview Manor Country Day School and sundry strays.

Mr. Banks thought in terms of old friends. As his memory limbered up, their dim forms passed before him almost faster than he could write them down. By the time he had finished with World War I his heart was overflowing with good-fellowship. Unfortunately, he couldn't remember the last names of many of them and was obliged to let them go their way. Then he could not remember where most of the balance lived (or if they did). As a result his list was a small one.

He spent the following evening combining the lists. There were alarmingly few duplications. Apparently the members of the Banks family had no friends in common. Finally he turned to his wife and daughter with a sadistic leer. "Guess how many."

Mrs. Banks squirmed uneasily. "Two hundred?" she ventured without conviction.

"Five hundred and seventy-two," shouted Mr. Banks triumphantly. *"Five! Seven! Two!* What did I tell you? It's either the immediate family or Madison Square Garden."

Mrs. Banks grabbed the lists. "Nonsense. Let me see. You've done something wrong. I'll bet *I* can cut this down. Now look here, we certainly don't need to have the Sparkmans. We never see them and as for that dyed-haired woman I don't care if I ever have her in my house again."

Mr. Banks wondered why it was that, every time he discovered an attractive woman, Mrs. Banks said her hair was dyed. And anyway what if it was? "Listen," he said. He was dignified now; cool, austere—and on guard. "Do you realize that Harry Sparkman is one of my most intimate friends, to say nothing of being a very good client? Why, I'd go to the ends of the earth for that fellow and he would for me."

"How ridiculous. You hardly ever see him."

"There you are," said Kay. "I *told* you these were just customers. I *knew* it."

Mr. Banks bit his lip and said nothing. He realized that he was licked

"Five hundred and seventy-two," shouted Mr. Banks triumphantly.

for the moment. "And who in the world are the DeLancey Crawfords?" continued Mrs. Banks smoothly. "I never even heard of them."

It was Kay's inning. "Listen, Mom. How can you be so *stupid*? Don't you remember that I spent half the *summer* with them at Western Point two years ago? And Twinkey Crawford is one of my *closest, closest* friends. Why, Mother, they've been right here in this *house*. Now if we're going on like *this,* Mother—"

"Maybe they won't come," suggested Mr. Banks. "Don't they live in Pittsburgh or someplace?"

"We can ask those families to the church and not the reception," said Mrs. Banks, disposing of the matter.

"The *church*!" cried Mr. Banks. "You mean to say you want to ask Harry and Jane Sparkman to the *church* and not to the *house*? Harry *Sparkman*? My intimate friend? Did *they* ask *us* just to the church when *their* daughter got married? No. And you were delighted to go to the reception. The *church*!"

The following evening Mr. Banks returned with a card file and large quantities of three-by-five cards.

"The pink are for 'Church Only,' " he explained. "The white ones are 'Church and Reception.' Now here's a rubber stamp. Whenever you're sure someone can't come because they live out of town or something, stamp that card 'P.N.C.' That means 'Probably Not Coming.' "

Three nights later everyone's name had been written on a pink or a white card. The out-of-towners and the local 4Fs had been happily stamped "P.N.C." Then Mr. Banks took the second census.

Mrs. Banks watched him nervously. "Maybe they'll come out about right now," she said.

Kay looked bored. "The whole thing is just *too* sordid. I had always thought a wedding was a *joyous* occasion. The way *you're* going at it you might as well hire a couple of *bookkeepers* to put it on for you."

Mr. Banks' only reply was to count audibly to help his concentration. "Here's the box score," he announced at last. "Ten people have been asked to the church and not the reception. Five hundred and sixty-two have been asked to both. There are one hundred and fifty-two cards stamped 'P.N.C.' That leaves four hundred and ten people who might show up. Figuring that a third of them won't, you'll have two hundred and seventy-three people at the reception."

"I don't follow you very well," said Mrs. Banks in a dazed voice, "but it looks as if we'd have to cut out a few."

"All you've got to do is to throw a hundred and twenty-three people out on their necks," said Mr. Banks grimly.

Kay yawned. "I'm going to bed. *My* list is right down to the *bone,* so I can't be of much help."

Mr. Banks opened his mouth, but Mrs. Banks motioned it shut again. Kay stalked out of the room, swinging her hips with dignity.

"We can work it out," said Mrs. Banks. "Kay's upset. All we have to do is to shift these superfluous people over to the church and not invite them to the reception. Now the Harry Sparkmans—"

Mr. Banks refused the gage. The timing didn't seem right. "All right," he said. "Let's go. We'll start by putting the Garden Club in the church—and leaving 'em there."

Each white card was removed from the box, debated at length, and returned to its original place with a sigh. At the end of each round, when they came to Carlton B. Zachery, they had succeeded in eliminating or relegating to the church only a handful of names. Quite obviously they were getting nowhere. They had too many dear, close, loyal, lifelong friends, to all of whom they seemed to be indebted.

Each white card was . . . debated at length and returned to its place with a sigh.

After three fruitless evenings of this sort of thing Mr. Banks had lunch with a client who was head of a large accounting firm. He had just run the gantlet himself and, after the manner of all survivors, he liked to strut his scars. As a form of wound-licking he had reduced everything to neat figures.

Wedding guests, he explained, should be broken down into church units and reception units. That was the only way to get at the per-unit cost. At his wedding each reception unit cost $3.72, including champagne, caterers, tips, breakage, flowers, furniture-moving and extra insurance. He had not included wear and tear, feeling that, considering the occasion, it would be on the mercenary side.

Mr. Banks made some calculations on the tablecloth, and the spirit of hospitality fled from him. That evening he had a business dinner in town, but the following morning he faced the shaving mirror with the set jaw of leadership.

He had reduced everything to neat figures.

Someone had to take the helm. Someone had to tie up this disintegrating situation before it fell apart completely. For three seventy-two a unit he would undertake to tie up a wounded lion.

"I'll tell you one thing, Ellie," he announced as he rubbed in the shaving soap vigorously. "Only a hundred and fifty people are coming to this reception. You've got to cut down the list. I don't care who you leave out. I don't care how many just get asked to the church. Pack 'em in. Build a grandstand in the chancel if you want. All I say is that the hundred and fifty-first person to enter this house gets thrown out on his ear even if it's your own mother."

Mrs. Banks looked at him with an astonishment that experience never seemed to dim. "Why, Stanley, that's what I said at the very beginning.

And you said it was an insult to ask anybody to the church and not the reception. I'm willing enough to cut and have been right along. Now people like the Sparkmans can just as well—"

Mr. Banks winced. "It's not a question now of insulting people. It's a matter of survival. What's the world going to say when we land in the gutter just because we insisted on giving a wedding reception like a Roman emperor? No sir. It's no use arguing with me now, Ellie. I've made up my mind. One fifty is the limit."

Things looked better after he had had his breakfast, but he didn't weaken. "Now, Ellie," he said, as he left the house, "I want you to take that list today and slash it down to a realistic basis. I leave it all to you."

He felt masterful and composed that evening as he entered 24 Maple Drive. Next to achieving sudden riches, acquiring financial equilibrium is almost equally gratifying.

"Got everything fixed up, Ellie?" he called into the living room.

"Yes, only—"

"Pops." Kay came out and threw a slim arm around his neck. "Pops, you big stupid. Do you know what you did? You forgot Buckley's list. It just came today."

Mr. Banks' psyche collapsed like an abandoned bathrobe. He walked slowly to the big wing chair and sat down heavily. "How many?" he asked. His voice sounded choked.

Mrs. Banks came boiling into action beside her daughter. "He couldn't have been cuter," she declared. "He only wants a hundred and twenty-five including *everybody*. And I mean that's *everybody*. And he's marked those that he doesn't think will come—like the officers in his squadron and so on."

"Oh, they've *got* to come." Kay clasped her hands ecstatically.

Mrs. Banks hurried on. "There are about fifty 'P.N.C.s' on the list. So that really cuts it down to seventy-five. And if you figure only two thirds of those will show up—"

"O.K.," interrupted Mr. Banks firmly. "That just means cutting seventy-five more from our list. If I haven't got a friend left when this thing is over—why, I haven't got a friend left—and that's that."

All evening the list was slashed. Everyone finally got into the spirit of the thing until bosom friends were thrown out with a whoop of joy. By eleven-thirty it was reduced to two hundred and four. If a third of those didn't come there would be one hundred and fifty-three at the house. Beyond that point they could not go.

Two nights later Kay came into the living room and sat on the arm of her father's chair. She ran her fingers through his thinning hair.

"Pops darling, are you going to miss me?"

He swallowed quickly and patted her knee. "Don't let's talk about it, Kitten. If you're happy, I'm happy. That's straight."

"You're so sweet, Pops." She kissed him lightly on the forehead. "Do you know something? I hate to tell you—but I've done the stupidest thing."

"Now what have you done? Mislaid Buckley?"

"No, Pops, but for the last few days I've been thinking of people I forgot. I mean *important* people. People that I'd have simply *died* if they hadn't been at the reception."

Mr. Banks sat up suddenly, his warm mood evaporated. "How many people?"

"Oh, I *knew* you'd be cross, Pops. I know it was very dumb. I'm afraid there are quite a *lot*."

"How many is that?"

"Well, maybe forty."

From this point on morale tended to disintegrate. So did the list. Each evening Mr. Banks thumbed through the "Church Only" cards with sad eyes.

"Bob and Liz!" he murmured. "If anybody'd told me Bob and Liz wouldn't be at my daughter's wedding reception I'd have said they were crazy. Remember the week ends we used to spend at their camp. Those were—"

"Why don't you ask them, Stan? I agree with you. It just isn't right not to have Bob and Liz. Why not make an exception?"

"Guess we should." Mr. Banks tore up the pink card venomously and carefully made out a white one. "Maybe a third of them won't come."

Or again: "Len and Louise Warner! Imagine what they're going to say. Our best friends. Three seventy-two a head. What price lifelong friends?"

"I know, dear. It's so cold and calculating when you put it that way. I should think lifelong friends were very cheap at three seventy-two a pair."

"A head," corrected Mr. Banks, transferring the Warners to a white card.

The pink cards gradually shrank. The white ones increased daily. Mrs. Banks' apprehensive look returned.

"I just don't see what's going to happen if all these people come," she said.

"They can go out on the back lawn," said Mr. Banks.

"Suppose it rains."

"It won't," said Mr. Banks.

The day came when the list must be sent to the lady who spent her life addressing wedding invitations in a copperplate handwriting. There was a last futile attempt to get it under control.

"Who are all these clucks?" fumed Mr. Banks, pawing through the cards. "I've never heard of half of them. Here I am throwing an Irish picnic for a lot of fuddyduds I never heard of."

"Well, they certainly aren't *my* friends," wailed Kay. "You all know I wanted a small wedding with just *my* friends. Now we seem to be putting on a *convention* or something."

"I know, dear," Mrs. Banks soothed. "It's a shame we don't have a bigger house. There are a lot of people I'd like to ask, I'll admit. For instance, it seems to me we've left out all of Mother's friends."

"Whoever these people may be," announced Mr. Banks quickly, "they are the Wedding Guests. The books are closed."

Gentlemen's Caterers All Are We

WE MUST do something about the caterer," said Mrs. Banks.

"The what?" Mr. Banks understood perfectly.

"Darling, did you think Delilah was going to handle the wedding reception all by herself?"

Mr. Banks couldn't truthfully say that he had thought about the matter at all—or that he wanted to think about it now.

"I've been finding out about caterers," continued Mrs. Banks in the bland tone of one conscious of having done her work while others fiddled. "The only thing to do is to have one come out from town. Sally Harrison had one for little Sally's wedding. She was crazy about him. His men were efficient and courteous and he's done a lot of weddings for people we know so he understands the sort of thing we want and she said he was very reasonable. Let's see. She gave me a card. I put it somewhere. Now let me think—"

Mr. Banks picked up his book, knowing that he wouldn't be troubled by the subject again for at least half an hour.

On the following Saturday morning Mr. and Mrs. Banks drove to town and visited the offices of Buckingham Caterers, specialists in luncheons, dinners, buffet suppers, cocktail parties, wedding receptions, christenings, lodge meetings and general social functions.

Mr. Massoula, who appeared to be in charge, was obviously a young man who knew his way about. He had a long upper lip decorated on its lower edge with a tiny mustache, reminiscent of a fringe on a lamp shade. His double-breasted, blue suit was sharply creased and his thin, black hair was plastered down so tightly that it might have been painted on his skull.

Wedding reception? Yes indeed. Buckingham Caterers were fully equipped to take the whole affair over. Mr. and Mrs. Banks didn't need to give the matter another thought. Just specify the date and they could romp off to the Arizona Biltmore or Palm Beach or Palm Springs

Mr. Massoula was obviously a young man who knew his way about.

or wherever it was that people like Mr. and Mrs. Banks spent their time. The point was they *did not need to worry.*

Buckingham Caterers had handled some of the biggest and most expensive weddings in the country. Mr. Massoula let it be understood clearly that they were not in the habit of putting their shoulder to weddings which were not in the upper brackets of the social scale.

"But first," said Mr. Massoula, reaching under the table and producing several large photograph albums, "I'd like to get your ideas about a wedding cake. Once the wedding cake has been established Buckingham Caterers take over. Now here is a very popular cake. That's Brenda Santanya. You know. Daughter of Princess Fraschisi by her second husband."

Mr. Banks looked at his wife. They hadn't even thought about a wedding cake. To Buckingham Caterers it was obviously not a matter for discussion. Mr. Massoula turned over dozens of photographs showing brides and grooms about to destroy hideous cakes of every size and shape. One could see that the cakes were different, but the brides and grooms all looked alike.

Mr. Massoula had an encyclopedic memory for names and social connections. The First Families of the nation passed in review before Mr. and Mrs. Banks. They had never heard of most of them, but they were pleased by the way that Mr. Massoula assumed that all these people were their buddies.

"That's one of Tommy Manville's weddings," he said. "We've done almost all of them. Good old Tommy. Delightful person, isn't he?"

Mr. Banks was about to say "Yes" but checked himself. He began to wish he had chosen a less socially prominent caterer.

"Ours isn't going to be a big reception," he ventured.

"Small and select. I understand perfectly. Buckingham Caterers can handle them any size."

Mr. Banks' fingers tightened on the edge of the table. "We don't want a cake," he said with dignity. Mrs. Banks' admiring glance fortified his courage.

"What! You don't want a cake! Why—"

Mr. Banks shot the works. "I think cakes are cheap," he said. "Every Tom, Dick and Harry has cakes. We don't want one."

Mr. Massoula looked at him with new respect. "I understand," he murmured. "It is true that the *very* select weddings no longer have them. We must show them, though. Most people wouldn't understand if we didn't."

"Of course not," said Mr. Banks. He dreaded the moment when he had to tell Mr. Massoula that this particular reception was to be held in a place called Fairview Manor.

Mr. Massoula brought up another large album from under the table. "While you're here I'd like to have you look at a few shots of some of our receptions."

As he looked Mr. Banks' dismay turned to panic. Buckingham Caterers not only dealt exclusively with the uncrowned heads of American Industrial Aristocracy, but apparently they catered only on huge estates and in palaces. He wondered how he could get out of the whole thing gracefully. Maple Drive had suddenly become a kind of suburban back alley. Quite obviously his home would look like somebody's gatehouse to Mr. Massoula.

But it was too late. Mr. Massoula had pulled out a pad of forms. "Now we should get some idea of what you would like to serve. We will supply the champagne of course."

Much to his chagrin Mr. Banks turned slightly red. "I'm sorry. What I mean is I didn't know. That is to say I've bought the champagne already."

Mr. Massoula's face clouded with politely restrained annoyance. "Then we will have to charge corkage, of course."

"Corkage?"

"A dollar a bottle for drawing and pouring."

"Oh, Delilah can take care of all that."

"If you are referring to one of your house staff," said Mr. Massoula firmly, "you must understand that in an affair of this kind the caterer takes over completely. Any other arrangement would cause friction in the servants' quarters. I am sure *you* understand, madam." He smiled at Mrs. Banks as mothers smile at one another over the heads of their wayward young.

Mrs. Banks returned the smile. "Indeed I do."

"By the way," said Mr. Massoula, "are you serving French champagne?" Had he said, "You are serving French champagne, of course?" the meaning would have been the same.

"As a matter of fact I'm not," said Mr. Banks in a tone that acknowledged the eccentricity of his decision. "I just think it's a shame to waste good vintage champagne on these kids. So I'm giving them American," he finished lamely.

Mr. Massoula nodded understandingly. "That will be all right with us," he said graciously. "Now, about the food. Let's see. The wedding is in early June. How about a large cold salmon at either end of the table with the various salads in great bowls in the center? Another dramatic arrangement is a cold sturgeon in the middle of the table. Now for the ices, we pride ourselves on a very special effect with colored electric lights embedded in a huge cake of ice, capped—"

"But," interrupted Mrs. Banks timidly, "we hadn't intended to have that kind of a reception."

Mr. Massoula gave her a puzzled look and laid down his pencil. "What did you have in mind, madam?"

Mrs. Banks fingered her handbag nervously. "Well, we thought that maybe some small assorted sandwiches—different kinds, you know—and ice cream and little cakes—"

"Of course you can have what you wish, madam, but that is usually what we serve at children's parties."

"Well, it's what we *want,*" said Mrs. Banks with a sudden harshness that in turn surprised her husband.

"Of course. Of course," said Mr. Massoula, making notes. "And I can assure you that you will be pleased when you see the results. Now where will the reception take place?"

"Twenty-four Maple Drive, Fairview Manor," said Mr. Banks belligerently.

"Is that a club or a country estate?" asked Mr. Massoula.

"It's my *home,*" replied Mr. Banks with dignity.

Mr. Massoula bowed slightly in deference to the generic sacredness of all homes. "What attendance do you anticipate?"

"About a hundred and fifty."

"Is it a large house?"

"No," said Mr. Banks defiantly. "It's a small house."

"Then of course you are planning for a marquee on the terrace."

"I have no terrace. If they overflow the house they can tramp around in the yard."

"And what if it rains?" asked Mr. Massoula with a rising inflection, glancing at Mrs. Banks. "What if it pours that day?"

"That's just what *I* said," put in Mrs. Banks. "Stanley, what *would* we do if it poured?"

"A marquee is very inexpensive," reassured Mr. Massoula soothingly, "and even if it doesn't rain you really *should* have it. I'll tell you what we'll do. I'll have one of our field engineers go over the property. We always have to do that anyway to study circulation problems and that sort of thing."

"Listen," said Mr. Banks desperately. "We've talked about everything but how much this is going to cost."

"The cost," said Mr. Massoula, "will be relatively small for a party such as you describe." His tone indicated that the kind of party which Mr. Banks had described wasn't much of a party. "For the *minimum* refreshments which you have specified the cost will be a dollar and a half a head, plus corkage, plus the cost of the marquee and sundry small expenses. For that Buckingham Caterers take *complete* charge, including experienced and courteous men who have been with us for years. Don't consider the cost, Mr. Banks. It will be trifling compared to the service which you will receive."

Apparently the social season was dragging a bit, for a few days later Mr. Massoula arrived in person at 24 Maple Drive. He was accompanied by a sheepish-looking character with handlebar mustaches, whom he referred to as Joe. Mrs. Banks assumed that he was one of the field engineers whom Mr. Massoula had spoken about, although he looked more like a horsecar conductor.

Mrs. Banks was a meticulous housekeeper and she had always been proud of her home. Now, as Mr. Massoula and Joe wandered from room to room with cold appraising eyes and occasional mumbled comments, she realized that neither of them had ever before catered in such a hovel.

"Small," said Mr. Massoula.

"I'll say," agreed Joe. "How many head did you say?"

"Hundred fifty."

"Jesus," said Joe. Mrs. Banks was afraid he was going to expectorate, but he refrained with an obvious effort.

"Circulation's bad," said Mr. Massoula.

"I'll say," agreed Joe.

"We'll have all the windows open on that day," assured Mrs. Banks.

"What *we* mean by circulation," said Mr. Massoula kindly, "is the

She realized that neither of them had ever before catered in such a hovel.

guest flow from room to room. A room with two interior doors has minimum circulation. A room like this with only one is—is—well, it's a death trap. Where does this go?"

Mr. Massoula pulled the knob of a door. It came off in his hands.

"I'm so sorry," said Mrs. Banks miserably. "It does that unless you push it in first. That just goes into a closet anyway."

Mr. Massoula placed the knob on the dining-room table. "Is this the pantry?" The two men seemed to fill the little room.

"Small," said Mr. Massoula.

"Dark," said Joe.

Mrs. Banks snapped the electric switch. Nothing happened.

"Bulb's busted," said Joe. "I seen enough."

Mrs. Banks followed them gloomily back to the living room.

"Circulation in this room's O.K.," said Mr. Massoula.

"Only one that is," said Joe.

"But you couldn't get more than a hundred and twenty-five in the house."

"Squash 'em like bugs if you did," said Joe.

"I'm planning to take a lot of these things up to the attic, you know," explained Mrs. Banks. "All those straight chairs go up, and the small tables and standing lamps, and we're thinking of taking up the rug."

"Takin' th' rug up ain't goin' to give any more room," said Joe. Mr.

The knob of the door came off in his hands.

Massoula maintained a displeased silence.

"Have you any suggestions?" asked Mrs. Banks nervously.

"Yes, madam, I have," said Mr. Massoula. "Even with a marquee you're going to be cramped. By the way, Joe, go out in the back and measure for the marquee. Now you see, madam, circulation's your big problem. The first thing you've got to do is clear this room of *all* furniture."

There was a suggestion of tears in Mrs. Banks' voice. "You don't mean the big davenport and the armchairs and—"

"Of course. *And* the piano. *Everything* must come out of this room. Now in the dining room—"

"Does the dining-room table have to go too?" she wailed, but Mr. Massoula was not listening.

"That chandelier over the dining-room table—could that be looped up or something?"

In view of the fact that the chandelier was not made of rubber tubing Mrs. Banks did not see how it could.

"Then you better have the electrician take it out an' cap it temporarily," said Mr. Massoula. "It's in the way. Now about these doors between the rooms. They've got to be taken off. You'd be surprised to see how much circulation you lose on account of doors. Especially doors like these."

Mrs. Banks might have forgiven him if he had not added that last sentence. As it was she lost her temper as an alternative to tears. "What in the world do you think I've got upstairs—a cold-storage warehouse? And who do you think is going to lug all this stuff up there—if there was room? And who do you think is going to get it down again?"

But Mr. Massoula was a creative artist. Details were not in his line. "We'll connect the marquee to this French door from the living room," he said. He tried to open the door but it merely slammed violently back and forth at the top. The bottom was apparently glued to the sill.

"It's stuck," explained Mrs. Banks. "I've been meaning to have that door fixed."

Mr. Massoula opened a window and leaned out. "Hi, Joe," he bawled. "Figure on a connecting angle through the French door here. Measure from the outside. The thing's stuck."

"I'll say," came an angry voice from the lilacs. "Too many God-damn bushes out here. Ought to get rid of 'em."

IV.

The Inner Man

By GLUYAS WILLIAMS

Breakfast in Bed

Out-of-the-Way Place

White-Collar Breakfast

V.

FROM

People of Note

By LAURENCE McKINNEY

THE CONDUCTOR

This Backward Man, this View Obstructor
Is known to us as the CONDUCTOR.
He beats the time with grace and vim
And sometimes they keep up with him.
But though they're eloquent and snappy
Conductors always seem unhappy.
Their strange grimaces on the podium
Suggest bicarbonate of sodium
May be, perhaps, the proper diet
To keep their inner fires quiet.
They have to think up countless capers
To keep them in the daily papers
Which help them in financial strictures
Or fit them for the motion pictures.
Conductors worry all the while
That's why they bow, but never smile.

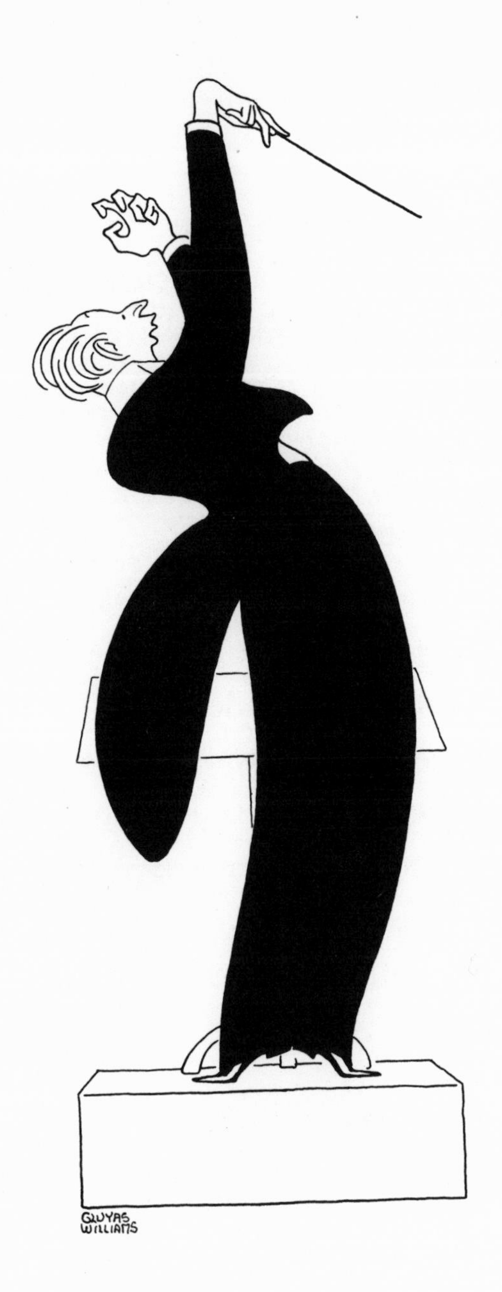
GLUYAS
WILLIAMS

HARP

If there's one lady in the bunch
To find her takes no special hunch
Nor sight particularly sharp
She is the girl who hugs the HARP.
The very longest tuner-upper
She has to have an early supper
And seated on a lonesome chair
Proceeds to wind up the affair.
Then she will sit and sit and wait,
Dispassionate and desolate,
Till the conductor's nod, or frown,
Sets her to stroking up and down.
And after these chromatic bits—
She simply sits and sits and sits.
A harpist must have lots of pluck—
A black silk costume—and a truck.

GLUYAS
WILLIAMS

PERCUSSION

When music gravitates to Russian
The noise you hear is called PERCUSSION
All clangorous and clattery
It's also called the Battery
Comprising gadgets—ten or more—
That clutter up a hardware store.
A fellow must be extra nimble
To beat a drum or crash a cymbal,
To bang a gong and in between
To tingle on the tambourine.
Eternal triangles, if missed
Will spoil a dainty thing by Liszt
And he must drag romantic tones
From glockenspiels and xylophones.
Far back and near the door they set him
So he escapes before they get him.

GLUYAS
WILLIAMS

THE WAGNERIAN SOPRANO

An awe-ful eyeful if you will
But here's another mouth to fill
Who may admit upon inquiry
To be an innocent Valkyrie.
Only great Wagner in "The Ring"
Could write the stuff she's built to sing
And only her pneumatic throat
Can sing the stuff that Richard wrote.
"Eva" and "Elsa," one agrees
Start but don't carry on with ease,
And it takes barrelfuls of breath
To function as "Elizabeth;"
So those who worship at their shrines
Are built on monumental lines
And while their voices rise, methinks,
The stage indubitably sinks.

GLUYAS
WILLIAMS

THE MIXED CHORUS

This motley mass we see before us—
This odd array—is called a CHORUS,
Or Glee Club, Choral Group or Choir,
Which Bach and Beethoven desire.
Sopranos, Altos, Tenors, Basses
Are rarely chosen for their faces
But for the strength which they employ
In shrieking out "The Hymn of Joy."
The keen-eyed listener often sees
Impending tonsillectomies
Or hears the twanging of the hordes
Of taut (and untaught) vocal cords.
One thing seems definitely certain
They should perform behind a curtain
And change the adage then to mean:
"Choruses should be heard not seen."

GLUYAS
WILLIAMS

VI.

The Visiting Public

By GLUYAS WILLIAMS

The house guests who don't mix, and thirty-six hours to go.

The cruising friends who unexpectedly take you up on an impulsive invitation of the previous winter to stop in sometime for hot food and comfortable beds.

The rainy weekend and the terrific out-of-doors guests.

The guests who get their dates mixed and arrive on the wrong weekend.

The guests with children who obviously aren't going to get along well with yours.

VII.

FROM

The Camp at Lockjaw

By DAVID McCORD

The Arrival

MRS. SUNWISE called it the camp, and would have referred to it as the cottage except that it was made of logs.

Mr. Sunwise called it the cabin, and sometimes the shack, because he could knock out his pipe on the floor and no one said anything.

Whatever Mr. Snivvely called it was done under his breath, for the last three miles had been up a pretty stiff hill and his feet were very sore.

"It's been a long pull," said Mr. Sunwise, dropping his pack under a pine tree and wiping his eyes and ears. A silence seemed to confirm this, and if there was the sound of a small expletive, that was only Mr. Snivvely slapping his eight hundredth mosquito and "easing off" his tump line, as little Richard would say.

Richard was nine, which was no particular reason why he should have been allowed to run on ahead out of sight with his sister Janet, aged eight. But he had done this more than ten minutes ago, and Mrs. Sunwise had told Mr. Snivvely that they always ran into camp that way, and that they would find them there when they (Mr. and Mrs. Sunwise and Mr. Snivvely) finally arrived. Mr. Snivvely, who at home was quite an amiable person, told himself he didn't care whether they reached it safely or not, and lightened his own pain by thinking up a horrible fairy tale, somewhat after Hänsel and Gretel and little Red Riding Hood, in which he was Bluebeard and the wolf, and Richard and Janet were making as much racket as they had all the way up on the train and in the old springless wagon on the tote road.

Mr. Snivvely had never seen the camp. He had never been camping. He usually stayed at the Ritz.

"We can all have a fine swim when we get there," said Mrs. Sunwise.

Mr. Snivvely remembered that he couldn't swim more than a dozen strokes, and said he would prefer a tub.

"There is no tub," said Mr. Sunwise.

Mr. Snivvely turned on the hot water of his mind and scalded everything of which he could think.

During the next mile hardly a word was said.

After that Mr. Snivvely sensed that they were nearing their destination. Mr. Sunwise would say "now just around this bend here," or "no, it must be the next one," or "when we cross the second gully," or "I remember this place," or "you could almost see it from here if those trees weren't quite so thick." He might as well have said "if the black flies weren't so thick."

All this was calculated to help Mr. Snivvely, who swayed a little as he walked. The effect, however, was much the same as if Mr. Sunwise were leading a martyr to the stake and kept trying to point out the pile of fagots.

In a patch of mud where the path crossed a trickle of water there were some tracks. Mr. Sunwise indicated with alacrity that three of them were made by a young buck and two by Janet's sneakers. Mr. Snivvely thought, without really putting his mind to it, that they were a good deal alike, and rather half regretted that the mud wasn't quicksand.

Once they lost the path, but that was when Mr. Sunwise tried to stalk a partridge, and Mr. Snivvely tripped on a root and fell with some violence and incidental noise. Mr. Sunwise explained to Mr. Snivvely that an Indian can walk in the woods without rustling a leaf or snapping a twig. Mr. Snivvely offered no comment on this.

During the last breathing interval on a bit of high ground from which, according to Mrs. Sunwise, you could "look right down on the camp there," Mr. Snivvely fanned himself with a few fern leaves and laved his neck with citronella. In a dejected sort of way he looked "down on the camp there," but all he saw was a chip of sky suggesting rain.

"It looks like rain," he said.

Mr. Sunwise said it didn't make any difference, for they were practically there anyway. Mr. Snivvely thought of his pajamas inside a very thin knapsack. This led him to examine for the first time the extra pack which Mr. Sunwise had given him and which he supported uncomfortably by means of the tump line referred to, a native device of leather which passed, like an old trunk strap, across his forehead and gave him a crick in the neck. He wondered what it contained, and could hardly struggle to his aching feet when Mrs. Sunwise told him he was portaging the personal effects of little Richard, including a toy motorboat, a baseball, two handy volumes on nature, several comics, the works of an

Mr. Snivvely failed for some time to comprehend that it was raining hard.

alarm clock, radio batteries, and a large rattrap to catch squirrels.

From then on Mr. Snivvely's strength failed notably, and had it not been for the shrill cries of welcome from Richard and Janet he would never have halted with the others, but struggled blindly on until he had fallen over the bank below the camp, to be swallowed up with a satisfactory gurgle in the quiet waters of the lake. What they shouted was "Hi-i-i," in terrific, vacational screams, with much dancing about, while Richard added, with a minimum of tact, that, gosh, Mr. Snivvely was "slow bringin' in that ole motorboat."

Mr. Snivvely, subsiding on the rotten plank of the second step to the porch, failed for some time to comprehend that it was raining hard, and that Mr. Sunwise had apparently forgotten the key to the door. He failed also to consider the fact that the windows were boarded up and fastened ingeniously from the inside. When this situation was brought to his attention over a couple of wet soda crackers, for Mrs. Sunwise thought that, really, they had better all have something to eat, Mr. Snivvely was roused to the point of looking at the resilient building, and when he had done this he asked himself how anybody should ever want to go into it even if it could be managed.

Little Richard suggested that he be allowed to drop down the chimney. Mr. Snivvely thought this a good idea, but the elder Sunwises were against it. Mr. Sunwise himself had the best plan.

"We shall batter down the door," he said.

So he and Mr. Snivvely set out in the rain to find a stone suitable for battering. It was funny, but there were no large stones in that part of Maine. So Mr. Snivvely and Mr. Sunwise went over to the eastern quarter of the state and returned a half-hour later hugging a huge boulder between them. Mr. Snivvely, at that point, would gladly have set out for home with his pajamas if he had only been sure of finding the way.

In the meantime Janet had skinned her knees in sliding off the porch roof, and although she cried rather softly it disturbed Mr. Snivvely to the point of desperation, so that after Mr. Sunwise had made a few passes at the Yale lock with sixty pounds of field stone, he was able to totter up and deliver the destructive power with a single stroke.

It happened that Mr. Snivvely and the rock which he was using went through the opening rather hastily, bringing up on the center table so that all the oil lamps which had been clustered on it the previous fall were knocked off and the chimneys broken.

Richard suggested that he . . . drop down the chimney.

Mrs. Sunwise, however, said it was good to be back; and after the boards had been removed from the windows, the broken glass cleaned up, and Janet's knees thoroughly painted with iodine, Mrs. Sunwise showed Mr. Snivvely his room. This turned out to be the air space behind a small partition, and offered all the secrecy of an individual bathhouse in a row of forty. Mr. Snivvely was told to make himself comfortable.

Mr. Snivvely and the rock . . . went through the opening rather hastily.

For some reason all the firewood had been used the previous year, and Mr. Poivrier, the French-Canadian trapper and guide who lived just a couple of lakes over, and who was to cut the summer's supply in stove lengths, had apparently forgot all about it. He had probably gone moose hunting instead. So Mr. Sunwise went out in the rain to gather old dry sticks, and Mr. Snivvely, after he had cleared some wild creature's nest from the corner of his room and brushed the dead bottle flies off the window sill, toppled across the shaky bed and went to sleep until he was awakened for what Mrs. Sunwise called supper.

The First Night in Camp

THE FIRST night in camp is a curious business. For some people it is like a comma in a divine sentence. For others it is a question mark. For Mr. Snivvely, the unhappy guest of Mr. and Mrs. Sunwise, it was an exclamation point.

It began very shortly after supper. Mr. Snivvely stood in the doorway watching the rain until a large drop, falling through a hole in the porch roof, put out his pipe. Mrs. Sunwise had said something about blankets, and these proved to be large bolts of a damp, moth-eaten material which were extracted from an old cupboard and hung up to dry. The room smelled of them, among other things.

At nine o'clock Mr. Snivvely said that if they all didn't mind he thought he would trot off to bed, which was about three yards away, and that he didn't care if the blankets weren't quite done (as he put it), for he was too tired to worry. It had occurred to him earlier to ask about sheets, but having once seen the blankets he felt that his unhappiness was already complete.

Ever since he could remember Mr. Snivvely had slept between sheets, with the possible exception of one or two times in college when he had stayed up all night. He had never felt a blanket with his bare feet, and the prospect was not elevating.

Mrs. Sunwise asked if he wainted a plain or a balsam pillow, and made a pun about sleeping on pines and needles. Mr. Snivvely chose them both.

Mr. Sunwise gave him a candle and made some joking remark about his not wanting anything to read. Mr. Snivvely did not laugh, and said "good night" with practically no emphasis on the adjective.

With the aid of this small light Mr. Snivvely then reconsidered his personal surroundings. On one wall hung a calendar, in colors, recommending that you buy your next suit at Sol's, the Outfitter. The subtlety of this suggestion was apparent in the attached portrait of a heavy sort

Mr. Snivvely . . . reconsidered his personal surroundings.

of lady standing at twilight under a waterfall. On the other wall was an unflattering kind of mirror and the first of a series of moths inducted from the deep recesses of the night. On the floor was a chair and a bed and Mr. Snivvely.

Mr. Snivvely was thankful that little Richard and Janet had been sent off early and that they were, to all purposes, sound asleep. At any rate, the radio (previously tuned to a noisy French program from Montreal) was silent. Mrs. Sunwise slept with the children at the other end of the cabin, but Mr. Sunwise had the cell next to his. Mr. Sunwise, with appropriate noises, was already going to bed.

Mr. Snivvely arranged his blankets as best he could, undressed himself, fixed the cover of netting over the bedposts, and blew out the candle. After he had blown it out he remembered that he had no matches with which to relight it, and the unpleasant thought kept him soundly awake.

This was unnecessary, because a number of organized frogs in the lake and an owl in a neighboring tree would have done it just as well, and even stood ready in case of emergency. The last thing Mr. Snivvely remembered was the drone of a June bug banging about the corners of his room. It was like a pea, he thought, rattling in an enormous pod.

He woke suddenly because something warm ran over his foot and dropped with a small thud to the floor. Mr. Snivvely kicked valiantly toward an unexplored corner of the bed, and was horrified to hear a chorus of small squeaks.

"Hello," called Mr. Sunwise sleepily, after Mr. Snivvely had hammered several times on the wall. "What's up?"

"I am," said Mr. Snivvely. "Do you know there are mice in here?"

"They won't hurt you," said Mr. Sunwise.

"They're in the bed," said Mr. Snivvely.

"Nonsense," said Mr. Sunwise.

"Bring me a candle," said Mr. Snivvely.

"You've got a candle," said Mr. Sunwise.

"I've no matches," said Mr. Snivvely.

"All right," said Mr. Sunwise.

So Mr. Sunwise brought in the matches, and a large hole was found in the bottom of the mattress. On deeper investigation a number of young mice were discovered, all very pink and shaven.

"I don't want them," said Mr. Snivvely.

Mr. Sunwise took the situation in hand.

"I don't believe there's anything else in there," he said, after a careful thumping.

"Do you think the mother will return?" asked Mr. Snivvely. "I've always heard they do."

"If you'd rather," said Mr. Sunwise, "I'll sleep here. You can stay in my room."

"What have you got in *your* bed?" asked Mr. Snivvely.

"Rats," said Mr. Sunwise.

"I can well believe it," said Mr. Snivvely.

"You're all right," said Mr. Sunwise. "You get some sleep."

"Where do you keep it?" asked Mr. Snivvely.

This ended the matter nicely. Mr. Snivvely crawled back into the scene of recent crime and fumbled for a while over page sixteen of the timetable. How civilized it looked! Then he counted the moths in the room. There seemed to be forty-six, not including five dead ones by the candlestick and a green bug on the ceiling which didn't qualify. The

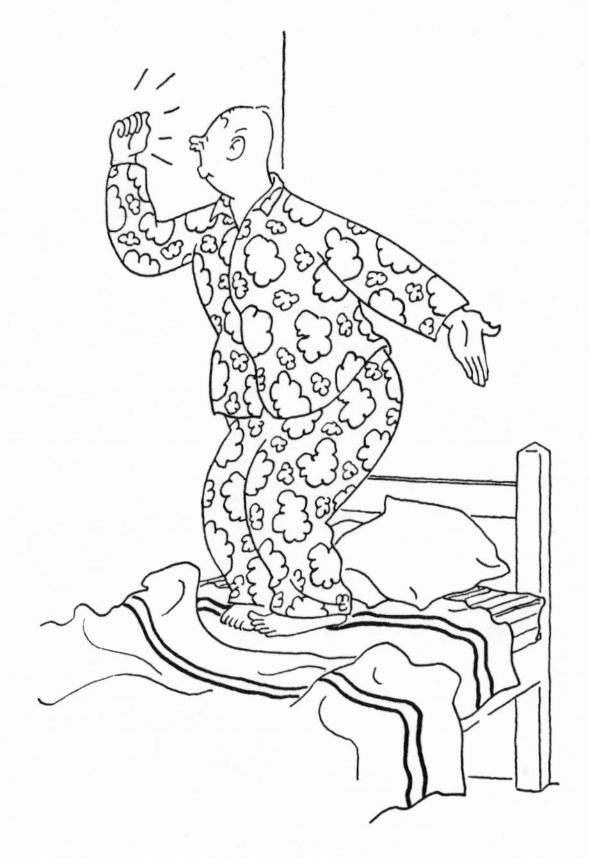

"Do you know there are mice in here?"

rain had stopped outside, and the fragrant odor of a skunk floated in. He was glad of the balsam pillow. He was sorry for nearly everything else.

In the next room Mr. Sunwise snored loudly in confident sleep. It was growing cold. Mr. Snivvely pulled the blankets up round his head, which left his feet out at the other end. In this way he lay till dawn, when he was startled by the unearthly laughter of a pair of loons. He would have referred it to Mr. Sunwise, for he had never heard anything at that hour louder than a robin or the milkman, but as long as it remained outside the window he determined not do to anything. For the first time he noticed an echo from across the lake. The echo of loon laughter is even more eerie than the laughter itself.

When the sun rose tentatively, Mr. Snivvely put his cold feet on the cold, bare floor and shuffled cautiously to the door. He could hear nothing inside the cabin but the sound of irregular breathing; so, with a basin of water in one hand and a sponge in the other, he proceeded to the porch. It was a beautiful morning, with a light mist rising from the lake and the air touched with bird song.

Mr. Snivvely splashed about almost in pleasure until he upset the basin with a crash.

"What's that?" called Mr. Sunwise from within.

"It's the basin," yelled Mr. Snivvely.

"It's only five," yelled Mr. Sunwise.

"I know it," yelled Mr. Snivvely, "I counted them carefully."

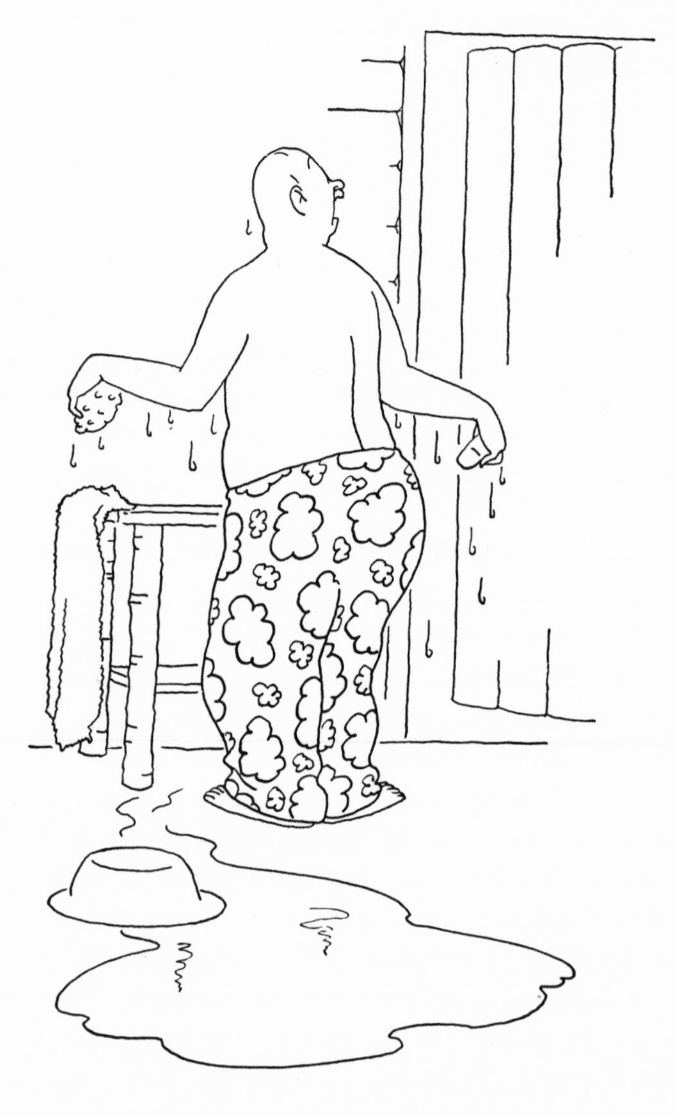

"It's the basin," yelled Mr. Snivvely.

"We don't get up till seven," yelled Mr. Sunwise.

"All right," called Mr. Snivvely. "You don't mind my washing a little?"

"A little *what?*" called Mr. Sunwise.

"Washing a little," repeated Mr. Snivvely.

"Go ahead," yelled Mr. Sunwise. "But don't make any noise. The family are still asleep."

"Not a sound," yelled Mr. Snivvely.

He had hardly time to get the soap out of his ears before the loons broke out again.

"I didn't do that," yelled Mr. Snivvely.

But Mr. Sunwise didn't answer.

Fishing Expedition

MR. SUNWISE and Richard were digging angleworms on the south side of the cabin.

Mr. Snivvely was looking on.

"When you dig up another, you'll have one," he said.

"We've got six and a slug," said Richard.

"I apologize," said Mr. Snivvely.

"They're all small ones," said Mr. Sunwise.

"The younger generation is the first to go," said Mr. Snivvely. "And by the way, Richard, I don't suppose you'd mind telling me where you got that tobacco tin you're using?"

"No," said Richard. "I found it."

"I'm sure of that," said Mr. Snivvely with suspicion. "I don't suppose you found it by any chance on the mantelpiece where I left it?"

"Yes," said Richard, "I did."

Mr. Snivvely's face hardened under his fresh sunburn.

"It had the last of my tobacco in it."

"It had the last of my tobacco in it," he said, addressing himself to Mr. Sunwise.

Mr. Sunwise uncoiled his spinal column and spoke sharply to Richard.

"It's all right," said Richard stoutly, "I poured it out in a pile on the edge of the porch."

Mr. Snivvely went off with a dwindling hope and came back with none. On the porch Mrs. Sunwise had said to him: "I wondered what that was when I swept it off."

Mr. Sunwise spoke sharply to Richard again and cut a worm in half.

Mr. Snivvely devoted himself to his temper.

"Anyway, you still have the tin," said Mr. Sunwise.

"I still have my reason," muttered Mr. Snivvely.

"What?" said Mr. Sunwise.

"Nothing," said Mr. Snivvely.

"Mr. Poivrier can bring in some more tobacco day after tomorrow. What kind do you smoke?"

"Not the kind he'll bring in," said Mr. Snivvely, who had inspected the stock of the village store.

Mr. Sunwise toiled in silence.

When Richard estimated that they had dug between thirty-six and forty-one worms, Mr. Sunwise put away his spade and they all went down to the lake.

Richard was to come along if he would sit still.

His father thought that no, he couldn't fish.

Mr. Snivvely was to have Mr. Sunwise's old bait rod (plenty good enough for a tyro) and Mr. Sunwise would take his best bamboo—a five-and-one-half ounce Sweetheart.

Before the latter was strung up, Mr. Snivvely was invited to "feel the whip of it."

Mr. Snivvely would have preferred to feel it across the posterior of young Richard, but he contented himself by snapping it viciously in the air until Mr. Sunwise took it away from him and asked him if he thought he was in a buggy.

"It's a fine rod," said Mr. Snivvely, who didn't know a reel from a leader box. By comparison, the shorter bait rod felt like a broken umbrella. He said as much.

"What you want," said Mr. Sunwise, "is a hat, a fan, a good cigar, and a lot of patience."

"I have a hat," said Mr. Snivvely, "and I don't smoke cigars. Also, thanks to Richard, I don't smoke a pipe."

In this amiable manner they climbed into the rowboat, and Mr. Sunwise pulled stubbornly for a spot below the horizon.

"It's a little early yet," he explained. "The trout don't move, as you've probably noticed, till along toward evening."

Mr. Snivvely said he'd come across one moving the night before. He had envied him.

"This is the biggest lake in the Lockjaw region," continued Mr. Sunwise.

"I suppose we're going to the farthest part of it?" inquired Mr. Snivvely.

"We're going where the fish are," said Mr. Sunwise. "Where I can use a fly and you can drop in a worm. There's a spring hole deep down, and you just might get a good one if they aren't rising. If they *are* rising, *I'll* get him!"

Mr. Snivvely asked him how *he* knew where the springs were, and would he mind not rocking the boat since he (Mr. Snivvely) could only swim up and down and the shore was in a to-and-fro direction.

They came to rest in a cloud of mosquitoes not many yards from land.

"Here," said (slap) Mr. Sunwise.

"Where?" said Mr. (slap) Snivvely.

For answer Mr. Sunwise pointed down into the water and put his finger to his lips with the implication that a trout might at any moment leap into the boat.

Mr. Snivvely and Richard peered over the side, and between them, somehow, the steel landing net fell overboard and sank quickly out of sight.

Mr. Sunwise was furious and said, "We might as well go home as fish without a net." This cheered Mr. Snivvely so much that he swore it was all his fault and not Richard's, and was there anything he could do, including the offer of his hat.

Mr. Sunwise (slap) said he was sorry to have lost his temper and that, after all, it was better (slap) for him to be upset than the boat; and with a calm, massaging stroke he slipped a worm on Mr. Snivvely's hook and told him to "drop it in off the deep end."

While Mr. Sunwise looped on a brilliant fly, and with long, anxious casts proceeded to cover all the vacant water in the vicinity, Mr. Sniv-

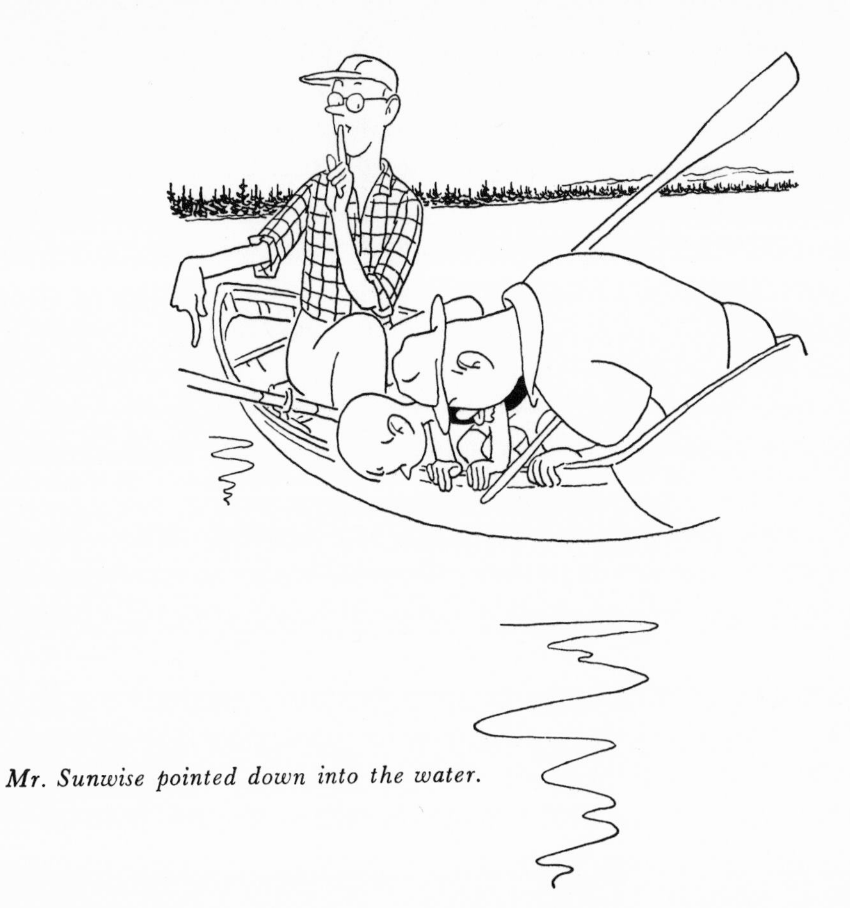

Mr. Sunwise pointed down into the water.

vely and Richard cowered in the stern and were eaten systematically by mosquitoes. A few circles finally appeared on the surface of the water, but the trout which made them were apathetic to the strategies of Mr. Sunwise, and the only contacts which he succeeded in establishing were with the upper branches of an overhanging tree, the exposed seat of Richard's trousers, and Mr. Snivvely's bait line which he would yank from the water just in the nick of time.

Mr. Snivvely asked incidentally what he was liable to catch besides trout. Mr. Sunwise mentioned every species but the shark, and said that depended: but whether on the worm or Mr. Snivvely or on both was not made clear. Mr. Sunwise was pretty cryptic about the whole business. He even failed to speak of the illegal aspect of the use of worms.

During the second hour Mr. Snivvely dropped in his twenty-sixth worm and his sunglasses simultaneously. From then on he was a hard man to deal with.

Once Mr. Sunwise, who had nearly connected with a trout, said that last year he had seen one jump right here which weighed five pounds.

"Did you see the five on its back?" asked Mr. Snivvely.

Toward dusk, when Mr. Snivvely was reduced to one large mosquito bite, he asked Mr. Sunwise what he thought that black speck in the distance could be.

Mr. Sunwise said he didn't know. Richard thought it was just a log. Neither was interested.

"I fancied it might be one of the oars," said Mr. Snivvely. "I haven't seen either of them for some time."

Mr. Sunwise came to like a shot and amazed Richard by the quality of his vocabulary. He said how the hell were they going to get home, and

Mr. Sunwise amazed Richard by the quality of his vocabulary.

Mr. Snivvely said he'd definitely given up all idea of getting home, and hoped, if Mr. Sunwise survived him, that he would see that his body was shipped back to his cousin Caleb, care of the First National Bank, and that he should explain to the coroner that it wasn't smallpox, really, but mosquito bites.

Mr. Sunwise told him to shut up for God's sake, and for the next half-hour they worked their way ashore with all available bare hands. Here they took aboard a few branches and propelled themselves by eight-thirty to the first oar. It was then too dark to look for the second.

"It's little events like those today which make the woods life what it is," said Mr. Sunwise in a genial mood that evening.

Mr. Snivvely pledged him in condensed milk, and dreamed all night with a great deal of pleasure first that a moose ate him and second that he was permanently injured in a taxicab smash.

Nature Walk

WHEN IT rains at Lockjaw, it usually comes down solid for two or three days—sometimes for four.

On the third wet morning Mr. Snivvely was looking over the dry shelf of books for the seventeenth time: *The Crimson Sweater, Dog Days in Algeria, How to Mend a Cello, The Old Farmer's Almanack 1897, The Rover Boys Awash, Kamp Kraft, Rhymes of a Rolling Stone, The Boy Psychiatrist, A Tale of Two Cities, Memoirs of a Sempstress, How to Tell the Fungi, Dirndl, Around the World in a Hansom Cab, The Second Jungle Book, The Best Jokes of 1903, Brace Yourself, Uncle Tom's Cabin, Dick Tracy, Freckles, The Encyclopaedia Britannica* (eleventh edition, Vol. 19-20, MUN to PAY), *Plane and Partly Solid Geometry, The Cruise of Moustika, How to Hook Rugs in Your Spare Time, Old Inns of Greenland, Everyman's Astrology, Everybody's Atom, Let's Build a Leaky Canoe,* and so on.

His weary eyes rested on a little volume about the lesser butterflies.

Mrs. Sunwise, humming a lesser song to herself, found him leafing through it.

"Why, I declare! Do you like butterflies?"

It was such an unexpected question that Mr. Snivvely said, "Yes. I mean, if they leave me alone."

"I like the Fritillaries," said Mrs. Sunwise.

"That's a Mexican dish," said Mr. Snivvely.

"You're thinking of *frijoles,*" said Mrs. Sunwise.

"So I was. So I am," said Mr. Snivvely.

"And the Monarch! Last year we saw loads of them one afternoon on the west portage. They were all congregating on the black mud and pulsing their wings."

Mrs. Sunwise pulsed her hands at her shoulders to illustrate. "You know the Monarch: orange-brown wings? *Danaüs archippus?*" Mrs. Sunwise had more Latin than she could translate.

"Timeo Danaos . . ." murmured Mr. Snivvely.

Mrs. Sunwise pulsed her hands at her shoulders.

"What's that?" asked Mrs. Sunwise, sensing a new species.

"Some Latin about some Greeks," said Mr. Snivvely.

"Oh," said Mrs. Sunwise.

Mr. Snivvely turned another page.

"So you like Fritillaries?" he said absently.

"Yes, I like Fritillaries," said Mrs. Sunwise. "And some of the moths. Have you ever seen a Luna?"

"No," said Mr. Snivvely. "Unless that's what was on the window sill in my room this morning."

"Was it green, with long tails?"

"It was dead," said Mr. Snivvely. "I didn't notice the tails. I threw it away, along with a couple of ants that were hoisting it up on their shoulders. They wouldn't let go."

"Ants are interesting," observed Mrs. Sunwise, "but I'm not overfond of them. We don't have many here."

"Why not?" asked Mr. Snivvely. "Don't they like it? Or can't they find it? If I were an ant, I bet I could find it. Especially if I were a termite."

"I tell you what," said Mrs. Sunwise. "If it clears this afternoon, we'll all go on a butterfly-botany-bird walk, not overlooking the funguses. Would you like that? Do you like funguses—I mean, fungi?"

Mr. Snivvely, who had overlooked every fungus except athlete's foot, said "No."

"But you'd like the walk?" pursued Mrs. Sunwise.

He usually confined his walking to getting out of taxicabs and into doorways, or out of doorways and into taxicabs, but he said, "Yes of course!" He would be going out—out and home—in a couple of days now. He would have to walk out over that terrible trail by which he came in. He would need practice.

So he said again: "Yes indeed."

The weather (clouds, rain, wind, mist, uncertainty) cleared during lunch (pea soup, ham, potatoes, pickles, dried apricots, tea).

The sun came out, conspicuous and hot.

Mr. Snivvely, clad in a light blue shirt, a soiled white duck hat, an ancient pair of slacks tucked into the high moccasins which he had purchased in Bangor—machine-made in St. Louis for Kansas woodsmen and which still hurt him—walked in a semi-vacuum surrounded by continual Sunwise patter and the limber wet branches of trees which soon soaked him to the skin.

Little Richard and Janet looked for newts (whatever they were) and for other undesirable things under stones and on the underside of branches or in hollow trees.

"What kind of nuts?" asked Mr. Snivvely.

"Not nuts—newts," said Mrs. Sunwise.

Richard and Janet liked the sound of that tremendously, so they chanted it for five or ten minutes: *"Not nuts—newts!* Not nuts—*newts!* Not nuts——"

Mr. Sunwise looked and listened for birds, and kept lending Mr. Snivvely his Japanese Navy binoculars (many diameters) and pointing out the Lockjaw avifauna just as they left the branch on which they had been sitting.

Mrs. Sunwise chattered about butterflies and botany, lecturing on the so obvious variation between flowers and leaves that looked to Mr. Snivvely's twig-lashed eyes so exactly alike. She was something of an authority on ferns and orchids, and explained a few of the fine points.

"The lady's-slipper is an orchid," she observed as they looked at one along the so-called trail around the lake. "A moccasin flower, if you like. It's very late for them."

It was lovely and lippy and fresh—not at all like Mr. Snivvely's moccasins.

"I miss the ribbon and the violet-headed pin," he said, rising somehow to the occasion.

"One of the queer things about the pileated woodpecker," Mr. Sunwise was explaining simultaneously, as he pointed to a large hole in a blasted tree, "is that he makes—according to some authorities—three kinds of holes: round, oblong, and (believe it or not) occasionally triangular. I've been looking for a triangular hole for a long while."

Mr. Sunwise generously described the pileated woodpecker: his notable size, field marking, flight, disturbing disappearance, and gradual return. "A beautiful, a noble bird," he concluded.

Mr. Snivvely, his eyes filled with the kaleidoscope of orange fungus, molds, mildews, rusts, smuts, fronds, fiddleheads, ferns, Fritillaries, hawk moths, Prometheas, various mosses, pitcherplants, pinnate leaves, corollas, calyxes, anthers, stamens; his ears filled with the fury of mosquitoes, and his nose with gnats and citronella, could do no more than wish the beautiful, noble bird a forest of lignum vitae and a shattered bill.

Janet found a cocoon wrapped up in a beech leaf, and her mother speculated on the kind of butterfly it would release.

"One spring—we were up here *very* early—the children got some hylas—you know—peepers—with a flashlight after dark. They put them in a Mason jar and for a week they piped all night. We just lay awake and listened. It was lovely."

It required several questions and detailed answers to assure Mr. Snivvely that no piping hylas would be captured in mid-July. The children's radio—normally tuned with deadly accuracy to French broadcasts from Montreal—was bad enough.

They walked ten yards in silence.

"I always have hoped," said Mrs. Sunwise half to herself as they stumbled ahead, "I have always hoped that I would someday discover a flower and have it named for me."

Mr. Snivvely named a flower for her on the spot, but he did it inaudibly.

When little Richard showed him his first newt—dainty, delicate, spotty, gentle, red, and innocent—he was beyond appraisal or applause. The newt didn't squirm, but walked quietly the length of Richard's small hand.

"Good," said Mr. Snivvely.

"A newt is an eft," contributed Mrs. Sunwise.

"Why does everything have to be something else?" complained Mr. Snivvely.

"They come out right after a rain," said Janet.

"I guess we've come out just before another rain," said Mr. Sunwise. "Those are thunderheads up there. This is the only place in the world where a thunderstorm can follow a wet spell."

But Mr. Snivvely was too uncomfortable to worry about weather, and began to walk to a rhyme which gathered a little moss as he rolled along the winding trail. He grew quite proud of it and finally said it out loud:

"The little newt,
So very mute,
Is not a brute,
A fish or fowl,
A kind of owl.
He doesn't howl . . ."

"That was a hobblebush," said Mrs. Sunwise brightly.

"Why, Mr. Snivvely," said Mrs. Sunwise, stopping in her muddy tracks. "You're a poet!"

It was the first compliment Mr. Snivvely had received since he arrived at Lockjaw, and he felt rather pleased with himself.

But not for long.

He tripped suddenly on a root and fell sprawling.

"That was a hobblebush," said Mrs. Sunwise brightly. *"Viburnum alnifolium*—honeysuckle family."

"Thanks so much! I hope I haven't bruised it," said Mr. Snivvely.

They paused at an old camp-site clearing to pick and eat a few ripening raspberries. Mr. Snivvely had never seen raspberries except on the table—with sugar and cream—preferably whipped cream. He pricked his fingers on a neighboring thistle and thought he was bleeding badly until Janet convinced him that it was mostly berry juice.

"While we're at it," chirped Mrs. Sunwise, "let me show you some of our native berries. That hobblebush you tripped over has coral-red berries."

They looked at bunchberries, checkerberries, and bearberries.

"They all have red berries," said Mrs. Sunwise.

Mr. Snivvely spotted some big blue fellows which could easily pass for huckleberries.

"Poisonous," said Janet, who had picked up the word.

He made a note to speak to the club steward about it. Toadstools for mushrooms, God knows what for huckleberries: there was more danger in nature than he suspected.

"The less I think of it," he observed at random, "the more certain I am that this is not the life for me."

"Want to see me get some spruce gum?" asked Richard, unclasping his thyroid hunting knife.

"No, no, thanks. I've had all I want of that." Mr. Snivvely rubbed the unslack part of his slacks.

"Golly! Here's where a bear has been clawing a tree!" Richard and Janet screamed and shouted in delight.

"Where? Why?" Mr. Snivvely saw the torn bark and the nasty gashes.

The children were right. Mr. Poivrier had shown them such a tree the summer before.

"Were they—was he—after honey?" asked Mr. Snivvely in unfeigned apprehension.

Bears, he had been told, live largely on honey. Honey, he had read somewhere, is manufactured in trees. Trees . . .

"That's not a dead tree," interrupted Richard. "That's a live tree. He was sharpening his claws."

Mr. Snivvely was about to ask what for, when he remembered that one must never get between a she-bear and her cubs. It might have been a she. It probably was. The sharpened she-bear undoubtedly had cubs.

He looked furtively about him. No one had a gun. No one else seemed the least anxious about not having a gun. Mr. Sunwise's father had had a gun in 1896. He darted a glance back over his shoulder, slipped on a wet stone, and fell into some black portage mud. He clutched at the nearest plant.

"Oh, look!" cried Mrs. Sunwise. "Mr. Snivvely's found a maidenhair fern!"

He staggered to his feet and half heard a brief lecture on the beauty and whalebone structure of this delicate fern's black stem.

"Not as black as this mud," he muttered with acerbity.

"Not as black as that cloud either," said Richard, pointing with alacrity.

Sure enough, Mr. Sunwise had been right. The shower was on them in ten minutes. Mr. Snivvely knew just enough not to get under a tree in a thunderstorm, but he had never faced the problem in the woods. There was of course nothing else to be under, whether you stood or walked or ran.

In ten minutes more the lightning was striking all around them. The thunderclaps deafened them, and it rained buckets and barrels. Mr. Snivvely prayed incoherently, and for the first and last time the camp at Lockjaw finally loomed before his eyes as a kind of synthetic palace, haven, bomb shelter, and subway entrance.

He followed the others into it in gratitude. In no time at all he was in bed and quite unable to see the beautiful double rainbow which Mrs. Sunwise described, arch by arch, as if it were a rare and exotic flower.

VIII.

America's Playgrounds

By GLUYAS WILLIAMS

Anywhere in Florida—Shuffleboard

New Hampshire Village, Winter

Coney Island

"Tourists Accommodated"

Pool and cabañas, Miami Beach

The Maine Coast

IX.

FROM

The Benchley Roundup

By ROBERT BENCHLEY

"Take the Witness!"

NEWSPAPER accounts of trial cross-examinations always bring out the cleverest in me. They induce day dreams in which I am the witness on the stand, and if you don't know some of my imaginary comebacks to an imaginary cross-examiner (Doe vs. Benchley: 482-U.S.-367-398), you have missed some of the most stimulating reading in the history of American jurisprudence.

These little reveries usually take place shortly after I have read the transcript of a trial, while I am on a long taxi ride or seated at a desk with plenty of other work to do. I like them best when I have work to do, as they deplete me mentally so that I am forced to go and lie down after a particularly sharp verbal rally. The knowledge that I have completely floored my adversary, and the imaginary congratulations of my friends (also imaginary), seem more worthwhile than any amount of fiddling work done.

During these cross-questionings I am always very calm. Calm in a nice way, that is—never cocky. However frantic my inquisitor may wax (and you should see his face at times—it's purple!), I just sit there, burning him up with each answer, winning the admiration of the courtroom, and, at times, even a smile from the judge himself. At the end of my examination, the judge is crazy about me.

Just what the trial is about, I never get quite clear in my mind. Sometimes the subject changes in the middle of the questioning, to allow for the insertion of an especially good crack on my part. I don't think that I am ever actually the defendant, although I don't know why I should feel that I am immune from trial by a jury of my peers—if such exist.

I am usually testifying in behalf of a friend, or perhaps as just an impersonal witness for someone whom I do not know, who, naturally, later becomes my friend for life. It is Justice that I am after—Justice and a few well-spotted laughs.

Let us whip right into the middle of my cross-examination, as I naturally wouldn't want to pull my stuff until I had been insulted by the lawyer, and you can't really get insulted simply by having your name and address asked. I am absolutely fair about these things. If the lawyer will treat me right, I'll treat him right. He has got to start it. For a decent cross-examiner, there is no more tractable witness in the world than I am.

I just sit there, burning him up with each answer.

Advancing toward me, with a sneer on his face, he points a finger at me. (I have sometimes thought of pointing my finger back at him, but have discarded that as being too fresh. I don't have to resort to clowning.)

Q—You think you're pretty funny, don't you? (*I have evidently just made some mildly humorous comeback, nothing smart-alecky, but good enough to make him look silly.*)

A—I have never given the matter much thought.

Q—Oh, you haven't given the matter much thought, eh? Well, you seem to be treating this examination as if it were a minstrel show.

A (*very quietly and nicely*)—I have merely been taking my cue from your questions. (*You will notice that all this presupposes quite a barrage of silly questions on his part, and pat answers on mine, omitted here because I haven't thought them up. At any rate, it is evident that I have already got him on the run before this reverie begins.*)

Q—Perhaps you would rather that I conducted this inquiry in baby talk?

A—If it will make it any easier for you. (*Pandemonium, which the Court feels that it has to quell, although enjoying it obviously as much as the spectators.*)

Q (*furious*)—I see. Well, here is a question that I think will be simple to elicit an honest answer: Just how did you happen to know that it was eleven-fifteen when you saw the defendant?

A—Because I looked at my watch.

Q—And just why did you look at your watch at this particular time?

A—To see what time it was.

Q—Are you accustomed to looking at your watch often?

A—That is one of the uses to which I often put my watch.

Q—I see. Now, it couldn't, by any chance, have been ten-fifteen instead of eleven-fifteen when you looked at your watch this time, could it?

A—Yes, sir. It could.

Q—Oh, it *could* have been ten-fifteen?

A—Yes, sir—if I had been in Chicago. (*Not very good, really. I'll work up something better. I move to have that answer stricken from the record.*)

When I feel myself lowering my standards by answering like that, I usually give myself a rest, and, unless something else awfully good pops into my head, I adjourn the court until next day. I can always convene it again when I hit my stride.

If possible, however, I like to drag it out until I have really given my antagonist a big final wallop which practically curls him up on the floor (I may think of one before this goes to press), and, wiping his forehead, he mutters, "Take the witness!"

As I step down from the stand, fresh as a daisy, there is a round of applause which the Court makes no attempt to silence. In fact, I have known certain judges to wink pleasantly at me as I take my seat. Judges are only human, after all.

My only fear is that, if I ever really am called upon to testify in court, I won't be asked the right questions. That *would* be a pretty kettle of fish!

"Ask That Man"

THIS IS written for those men who have wives who are constantly insisting on their asking questions of officials.

For years I was troubled with the following complaint: Just as soon as we started out on a trip of any kind, even if it were only to the corner of the street, Doris began forcing me to ask questions of people. If we weren't quite sure of the way: "Why don't you ask that man? He could tell you." If there was any doubt as to the best place to go to get chocolate ice-cream, she would say, "Why don't you ask that boy in uniform? He would be likely to know."

I can't quite define my aversion to asking questions of strangers. From snatches of family battles which I have heard drifting up from railway stations and street corners, I gather that there are a great many men who share my dislike for it, as well as an equal number of women who, like Doris, believe it to be the solution of most of this world's problems. The man's dread is probably that of making himself appear a pest or ridiculously uninformed. The woman's insistence is based probably on experience which has taught her that *any*one, no matter who, knows more about things in general than her husband.

Furthermore, I never know exactly how to begin a request for information. If I preface it with, "I beg your pardon!" the stranger is likely not to hear, especially if he happens to be facing in another direction, for my voice isn't very reliable in crises and sometimes makes no intelligible sound at all until I have been talking for fully a minute. Often I say, "I beg your pardon!" and he turns quickly and says, "What did you say?" Then I have to repeat, "I beg your pardon!" and he asks, quite naturally, "What for?" Then I am stuck. Here I am, begging a perfect stranger's pardon, and for no apparent reason under the sun. The wonder is that I am not knocked down oftener.

It was to avoid going through life under this pressure that I evolved the little scheme detailed herewith. It cost me several thousand dollars, but Doris is through with asking questions of outsiders.

I gather that there are a great many men who share my dislike for it.

We had started on a little trip to Boston. I could have found out where the Boston train was in a few minutes had I been left to myself. But Doris never relies on the signs. Someone must be asked, too, just to make sure. Confronted once by a buckboard literally swathed in banners which screamed in red letters, "This bus goes to the State Fair Grounds," I had to go up to the driver (who had on his cap a flag reading "To the State Fair Grounds") and ask him if this bus surely went to the State Fair Grounds. He didn't even answer me.

So when Doris said, "Go and ask that man where the Boston train leaves from," I gritted my teeth and decided that the time had come. Simulating conversation with him, I really asked him nothing, and returned to Doris, saying, "Come on. He says it goes from Track 10."

My voice isn't very reliable in crises.

Eight months later we returned home. The train that left on Track 10 was the Chicago Limited, which I had taken deliberately. In Chicago I again falsified what "the man" told me, and instead of getting on the train back to New York we went to Little Rock, Arkansas. Every time I had to ask where the best hotel was, I made up information which brought us out into the suburbs, cold and hungry. Many nights we spent wandering through the fields looking for some place that never existed, or else in the worst hotel in town acting on what I said was the advice of "that kind-looking man in uniform."

From Arkansas, we went into Mexico, and once, guided by what I told her had been the directions given me by the man at the news-stand in Vera Cruz, we made a sally into the swamps of Central America, or whatever that first republic is on the way south. After that, Doris began to lose faith in what strange men could tell us. One day, at a little station in Mavicos, I said, "Wait a minute, till I ask that man what is the best way to get back into America," and she said sobbing, "Don't ask anybody. Just do what you think is best." Then I knew that the fight was over. In ten days I had her limp form back in New York and from that day to this she hasn't once suggested that I ask questions of a stranger.

The funny part of it is, I constantly find myself asking them. I guess the humiliation came in being told to ask.

Editha's Christmas Burglar

IT WAS the night before Christmas, and Editha was all agog. It was all so exciting, so exciting! From her little bed up in the nursery she could hear Mumsey and Daddy downstairs putting the things on the tree and jamming her stocking full of broken candy and oranges.

"Hush!" Daddy was speaking. "Eva," he was saying to Mumsey, "it seems kind of silly to put this ten-dollar gold piece that Aunt Issac sent to Editha into her stocking. She is too young to know the value of money. It would just be a bauble to her. How about putting it in with the household money for this month? Editha would then get some of the food that was bought with it and we would be ten dollars in."

Dear old Daddy! Always thinking of someone else! Editha wanted to jump out of bed right then and there and run down and throw her arms about his neck, perhaps shutting off his wind.

"You are right, as usual, Hal," said Mumsey. "Give me the gold piece and I will put it in with the house funds."

"In a pig's eye I will give you the gold piece," replied Daddy. "You would nest it away somewhere until after Christmas and then go out and buy yourself a muff with it. I know you, you old grafter." And from the sound which followed, Editha knew that Mumsey was kissing Daddy. Did ever a little girl have two such darling parents? And, hugging her Teddy bear close to her, Editha rolled over and went to sleep.

She awoke suddenly with the feeling that someone was downstairs.

It was quite dark and the radiolite traveling clock which stood by her bedside said eight o'clock, but, as the radiolite traveling clock hadn't been running since Easter, she knew that that couldn't be the right time. She knew that it must be somewhere between three and four in the morning, however, because the blanket had slipped off her bed, and the blanket always slipped off her bed between three and four in the morning.

And now to take up the question of who it was downstairs. At first she thought it might be Daddy. Often Daddy sat up very late working on a case of Scotch and at such times she would hear him downstairs counting to himself. But whoever was there now was being very quiet. It was only when he jammed against the china cabinet or joggled the dinner gong that she could tell that anyone was there at all. It was evidently a stranger.

Of course, it might be that the old folks had been right all along and that there really was a Santa Claus after all, but Editha dismissed this supposition at once. The old folks had never been right before and what chance was there of their starting in to be right now, at their age? None at all. It couldn't be Santa, the jolly old soul!

It must be a burglar then! Why, to be sure! Burglars always come around on Christmas Eve and little yellow-haired girls always get up and go down in their nighties and convert them. Of course! How silly of Editha not to have thought of it before!

With a bound the child was out on the cold floor, and with another bound was back in bed again. It was too cold to be fooling around without slippers on. Reaching down by the bedside, she pulled in her little fur foot-pieces which Cousin Mabel had left behind by mistake the last time she visited Editha, and drew them on her tiny feet. Then out she got and started on tip-toe for the stairway.

She did hope that he would be a good-looking burglar and easily converted, because it was pretty gosh-darned cold, even with slippers on, and she wished to save time.

As she reached the head of the stairs, she could look down into the living room where the shadow of the tree stood out black against the gray light outside. In the doorway leading into the dining room stood a man's figure silhouetted against the glare of an old-fashioned burglar's lantern which was on the floor. He was rattling silverware. Very quietly, Editha descended the stairs until she stood quite close to him.

"Hello, Mr. Man!" she said.

The burglar looked up quickly and reached for his gun.

"Who the hell do you think you are?" he asked.

"I'se Editha," replied the little girl in the sweetest voice she could summon, which wasn't particularly sweet at that as Editha hadn't a very pretty voice.

"Hello, Mr. Man!" she said.

"You's Editha, is youse?" replied the burglar. "Well, come on down here. Grandpa wants to speak to you."

"Youse is not my Drandpa," said the tot, getting her baby and tough talk slightly mixed. "Youse is a dreat, bid burglar."

"All right, kiddy," replied the man. "Have it your own way. But come on down. I want ter show yer how yer kin make smoke come outer yer eyes. It's a Christmas game."

"This guy is as good as converted already," thought Editha to herself. "Right away he starts wanting to teach me games. Next he'll be telling me I remind him of his little girl at home."

So with a light heart she came the rest of the way downstairs, and stood facing the burly stranger.

"Sit down, Editha," he said, and gave her a hearty push which sent her down heavily on the floor. "And stay there, or I'll mash you one on that baby nose of yours."

This was not in the schedule as Editha had read it in the books, but it doubtless was this particular burglar's way of having a little fun. He *did* have nice eyes, too.

"Dat's naughty to do," she said, scoldingly.

"Yeah?" said the burglar, and sent her spinning against the wall. "I guess you need attention, kid. You can't be trusted." Whereupon he slapped the little girl. Then he took a piece of rope out of his bag and tied her up good and tight, with a nice bright bandana handkerchief around her mouth, and trussed her up on the chandelier.

"Now hang there," he said, "and make believe you're a Christmas present, and if you open yer yap, I'll set fire to yer."

Then, filling his bag with the silverware and Daddy's imitation sherry, Editha's burglar tip-toed out by the door. As he left, he turned and smiled. "A Merry Christmas to all and to all a Good Night," he whispered, and was gone.

And when Mumsey and Daddy came down in the morning, there was Editha up on the chandelier, sore as a crab. So they took her down and spanked her for getting out of bed without permission.

"A Merry Christmas to all and to all a Good Night!"

Throwing Back the European Offensive

THIS IS probably the hardest time of year for those of us who didn't go to Europe last summer. It was bad enough when the others were packing and outlining their trips for you. It was pretty bad when the postcards from Lausanne and Venice began coming in. But now, in the fall, when the travelers are returning with their Marco Polo travelogs, now is when we must be brave and give a cheer for the early frost.

There are several ways to combat this menace of returning travelers. The one that I have found most effective is based on the old football theory that a strong offense is the best defense. I rush them right off their feet, before they can get started.

In carrying out this system, it is well to remember that very few travelers know anything more about the places they have visited than the names of one hotel, two points of interest, and perhaps one street. You can bluff them into insensibility by making up a name and asking them if they saw that when they were in Florence. My whole strategy is based on my ability to make up names. You can do it, too, with practice.

Thus, let us say that I am confronted by Mrs. Reetaly who has just returned from a frantic tour of Spain, southern France, and the Ritz Hotel, Paris. You are inextricably cornered with her at a tea, or beer night, or something. Following is a transcript of the conversation. (Note the gathering power of my offense.)

MRS. R.: Well, we have just returned from Europe, and everything seems so strange here. I simply can't get used to our money.

MR. B.: I never see enough of it to get used to it myself. (*Just a pleasantry.*)

MRS. R.: When we were in Madrid, I just gave up trying to figure out the Spanish money. You see, they have *pesetas* and—

MR. B.: A very easy way to remember Spanish money is to count ten *segradas* to one *mesa,* ten *mesas* to one *rintilla* and twenty *rintillas* to one *peseta.*

A strong offensive is the best defense.

Mrs. R.: Oh, you have been to Spain? Did you go to Toledo?

Mr. B.: Well, of course, Toledo is just the beginning. You pushed on to Mastilejo, of course?

Mrs. R.: Why—er—no. We were in quite a hurry to get to Granada and—

Mr. B.: You didn't see Mastilejo? That's too bad. Mastilejo is Toledo multiplied by a hundred. Such mountains! Such coloring! Leaving Mastilejo, one ascends by easy stages to the ridge behind the town from which is obtained an incomparable view of the entire Bobadilla Valley. It was here that, in 1476, the Moors—

Mrs. R.: The Moorish relics in Granada—

Mr. B.: The Moorish relics in Granada are like something you buy from Sears Roebuck compared to the remains in Tuna. You saw Tuna, of course?

Mrs. R.: Well, no (*lying her head off*), we were going there, but Harry thought that it would just be repeating what—

Mr. B.: The biggest mistake of your life, Mrs. Reetaly, the biggest mistake of your life! Unless you have seen Tuna, you haven't seen Spain.

Mrs. R.: But Carcassonne—

Mr. B.: Ah, Carcassonne! Now you're talking! Did you ever see anything to beat that old diamond mill in the *Vielle Ville*? Would they let you go through it when you were there?

Mrs. R.: Why, I don't think that we saw any old diamond mill. We saw an old—

Mr. B.: I know what you're going to say! You saw the old wheat sifter. Isn't that fascinating? Did you talk with the old courier there?

Mrs. R.: Why, I don't remember—

Mr. B.: And the hole in the wall where Louis the Neurotic escaped from the Saracens?

Mrs. R.: Yes, wasn't that—? (*Very weak.*)

Mr. B.: And the stream where they found the sword and buckler of the Man with the Iron Abdomen?

Mrs. R. (*edging away*) : Yes, indeed.

Mr. B.: And old Vastelles? You visited Vastelles, surely? . . . Mrs. Reetaly, come back here, please! I just love talking over these dear places with someone who has just been there. . . . May I call on you some day soon and we'll just have a feast of reminiscence? . . . Thank you. How about tomorrow?

And from that day to this, I am never bothered by Mrs. Reetaly's European trip, and you needn't be, either, if you will only study the above plan carefully.

The other method is based on just the opposite theory—that of no offense, or defense, at all. It is known as "dumb submission," and should be tried only by very phlegmatic people who can deaden their sensibilities so that they don't even hear the first ten minutes of the traveler's harangue. The idea is to let them proceed at will for a time and then give unmistakable evidence of not having heard a word they have said. Let us say that Mr. Thwomly has accosted me on the train.

Mr. T.: It certainly seems funny to be riding in trains like this again. We have been all summer in France, you know, and those French trains are all divided up into compartments. You get into a compartment—*compartimon,* they call them—and there you are with three or five other people, all cooped up together. On the way from Paris to Marseilles we had a funny experience. I was sitting next to a Frenchman who was getting off at Lyons—Lyons is about half way between Paris and Marseilles—and he was dozing when we got in. So I—

Mr. B.: Did you get to France at all when you were away?

Mr. T.: This was in *France* that I'm telling you about. On the way from Paris to Marseilles. We got into a railway carriage—

Mr. B.: The railway carriages there aren't like ours here, are they?

I've seen pictures of them, and they seem to be more like compartments of some sort.

Mr. T. (*a little discouraged*) : That was a French railway carriage I was just describing to you. I sat next to a man—

Mr. B.: A Frenchman?

Mr. T.: Sure, a Frenchman. That's the *point.*

Mr. B.: Oh, I see.

Mr. T.: Well, the Frenchman was asleep, and when we got in I stumbled over his feet. So he woke up and said something in French, which I couldn't understand, and I excused myself in English, which *he* couldn't understand, but I saw by his ticket that he was going only as far as Lyons—

Mr. B.: You were across the border into France, then?

Mr. T. (*giving the whole thing up as a bad job*) : And what did *you* do this summer?

Whichever way you pick to defend yourself against the assaults of people who want to tell you about Europe, don't forget that it was I who told you how. I'm going to Europe myself next year, and if you try to pull either of these systems on *me* when I get back, I will recognize them at once, and it will just go all the harder with you. But, of course, *I* will have something to tell that will be worth hearing.

Inter-office Memo

IT WILL always be a mystery to me why I was asked "into conference" in the first place. I am more the artistic type, and am seldom consulted on the more practical aspects of life. I have given up wearing soft collars and can smoke a cigar, if it is a fairly short one, but I don't seem able to give off any impression of business stability. I am just one of the world's beautiful dreamers.

So when McNulty called me up and asked me if I could come over to his office for a conference with somebody named Crofish or Cronish of Detroit, I was thrown into a fever of excitement. At last I was going to sit in on a big business conference! I think there was some idea that I, as a hay-fever sufferer, might have a suggestion or two on handkerchiefs that might be valuable. For the conference was on the marketing of a steel handkerchief which the Detroit people were about to put out.

So all in a flutter I rushed over to McNulty's office, determined to take mental notes on the way in which real business men disposed of real business in the hope that one day I might extricate myself from the morass of inefficiency in which I was living and perhaps amount to something in the business world. At least, I would have caught a glimpse of how things ought to be done.

Mr. Crofish or Cronish (whose name later turned out to be Crolish) was already there, with his briefcase open in front of him and a lot of papers piled up on the desk. He and McNulty were both so bustly and efficient-looking that it hardly seemed worth while for me to sit down. This conference couldn't last more than a minute and a half!

"Sorry to bother you, Bob, old man," said McNulty, briskly, "but we thought that you might be able to help us out a little in this scheme for getting the Beau Brummel Steel Handkerchief before the public . . . Sit down won't you? . . . Perhaps Mr. Crolish can state his problem better than I can, and then we will get your angle on it."

Mr. Crolish looked at his papers and cleared his throat. "Well, here is the situation we are faced with," he began.

"Just a minute, Mr. Crolish," interrupted McNulty, "I think it might be well, before you begin, to find out from Reemis just what magazines we are going to use, so that Mr. Benchley will have a little better idea of what type of copy we shall need." And he turned to the telephone. "Get me Mr. Reemis, will you please, Miss Fane?"

Mr. Reemis's line seemed to be busy, so McNulty propped the receiver up against his ear and reached in the drawer for some cigars, while waiting.

"Another couple of days like this and spring will be here," he announced tentatively.

"That's right," said Mr. Crolish, which didn't leave much for me to say unless I wanted to fight the statement.

Mr. Reemis was very busy, so McNulty, still holding the receiver, tried something else to pass the time.

"Mrs. McNulty and I saw one of the worst shows I've ever seen last night. *Rolling Raisins.* Did you ever see it?"

I said that I hadn't and Mr. Crolish said that he hadn't but that he had heard about it.

"No wonder people don't go to the theatre more," said McNulty, "when they put . . . oh, hello! . . . Reemis? . . . say, could you step into my office for just a minute, please?"

While we were waiting for Mr. Reemis, McNulty explained the plot of *Rolling Raisins.* And, as Mr. Reemis was evidently coming into the office by a route which led him down into the street and up the back stairway, Mr. Crolish told the plot of a show which had opened in Detroit last week. I had just started in on the plot of a show we had once put on in college when Mr. Reemis appeared.

"This is Mr. Benchley, Mr. Reemis . . . I guess you know Mr. Crolish. . . . What we wanted to find out was just what magazines we are going to use in this Beau Brummel campaign."

"Well, there have been some changes made since we went over it with you, Mr. McNulty," said Mr. Reemis. "I'm not quite sure of the list as it stands. I'll shoot back to my desk and get it."

So Mr. Reemis shot back, and Mr. Crolish walked over to the window.

"They certainly are tearing up this old town, aren't they?" he asked. "Every time I come here there is a new building up somewhere. I suppose they'll be tearing down the Woolworth Building next."

"I understand they've started already," said McNulty, "but they don't quite know where to begin."

This was a pretty fair line and it got all the laugh that it deserved. The thing was beginning to take on the air of one of those easy-going off-hours which we impractical artists indulge in when we are supposed to be working. It was interrupted by Mr. Reemis shooting back with the list.

"Here we are," he said, brightly. "Now, as I understand it, this is a strictly class appeal we are trying to make and we don't want to bother with the old-fashioned handkerchief users, so we thought that—"

Here the door opened and one of the partners came in.

"Sorry to butt in, Harry," he said, "but have you seen this statement of the Mackbolter people in the *Times*?"

"I just glanced at it," said McNulty, ". . . you know Mr. Benchley,

Two young men bearing a layout came in.

Mr. Wamser? . . . I guess you know Crolish."

Mr. Wamser and I shook hands.

"Are you any relation to the Benchley who used to live in Worcester?" he asked.

I admitted that I had relatives in Worcester.

"I'll never forget the night I spent in Worcester once," he said, seating himself on the edge of McNulty's desk. "We were motoring to Boston and a thunderstorm came up; so we put in at Worcester—what's the name of that hotel?"

"The Bancroft?" I suggested.

"I don't think it was the Bancroft," he said. "What are some of the others? I'll know the name if I hear it."

I said that so far as I knew there weren't any others since the old Bay State House had been torn down.

"Well, maybe it was the Bancroft."

Mr. Crolish suggested that it might have been the Worthy.

"The Worthy is in Springfield," said McNulty.

At this point two young gentlemen bearing a layout came in.

"Sorry to interrupt," said one of them, "but do you want the package played up in this Meer-o page or just show the girl playing tennis?"

The two young gentlemen were introduced and turned out to be Mr. Rollik and Mr. MacNordfy.

"Hoagman is handling that more than I am," said Mr. Wamser. And going to the telephone he asked to have Mr. Hoagman step into Mr. McNulty's office for a minute. While waiting for Mr. Hoagman, Mr. Rollik asked the gathering (which was, by now, assuming the proportions of a stag smoker) if they had seen what Will Rogers had in the paper that morning.

"I can always get a laugh out of that guy Rogers," said Mr. Crolish.

"What I like about him is that he gets a lot of common sense into his gags. They *mean* something." It was Mr. MacNordfy who thought this.

"Abe Martin is the one I like," said McNulty. Mr. Wamser was of the opinion that no one had ever been able to touch Mr. Dooley. To prove his point he quoted a fairish bit of one of Mr. Dooley's dissertations in very bad Irish dialect. Mr. Hoagman, having entered during the recitation, waived the formality of introductions and began:

"If you like Irish jokes, I heard one yesterday that I thought was pretty clever. I may be wrong."

I made unnoticed for the elevator.

He was wrong, and so got down to business. "What was it you wanted to see me about?" he asked, as soon as he had stopped laughing.

"The boys here want to know whether the Meer-o people want the package played up in this layout or to subordinate it to the girl playing tennis?"

"Oh, you've got to play the package up," said Mr. Hoagman, thereby making the first business decision of the morning. This gave him such a feeling of duty-done that he evidently decided to knock off work for the rest of the morning and devote his time to story-telling.

The room was so full by this time that I had completely lost sight of Mr. Crolish, who was, at best, a small man and was in his original seat on the other side of the room, still sitting in front of his open briefcase. Mr. McNulty was talking on the telephone again and seemed good for fifteen minutes of it. The rest of the staff were milling about, offering each other cigarettes, telling anecdotes and in general carrying on the nation's business.

I looked at my watch and found that I was already late for a lunch date; so picking up my hat, I elbowed my way quietly out of the room unnoticed and made the elevator.

Later in the week I heard that McNulty had told someone that I was a nice guy but that there was no sense in trying to do business with me. I guess I shall always be just a dreamer.

Back to the Game

THIS IS about the time of year (it would be a good joke on me if this chapter were held over until Spring) when the old boys begin thinking of going back to college to the Big Game. All during the year they have never given a thought to whether they were alumni of Yale or the New York Pharmaceutical College, but as soon as the sporting pages begin telling about O'Brienstein of Harvard and what a wonderful back he is, all Harvard men with cigar ashes on their waistcoats suddenly remember that they went to Harvard and send in their applications for the Yale Game. There is nothing like a college education to broaden a man.

Going back to the old college town is something of an ordeal, in case you want to know. You think it's going to be all right and you have a little dream-picture of how glad the boys will be to see you. "Weekins, 1914," you will say, and there will be a big demonstration, with fireworks and retchings. The word will go round that Weekins, 1914, is back and professors in everything but Greek will say to their classes, "Dismissed for the day, gentlemen. Weekins, 1914, is back!" And a happy crowd of boys will rush pell-mell out of the recitation hall and down to the Inn to take the horses from your carriage (or put horses into it) and drag you all around the Campus. (My using the word "Campus" is just a concession to the rabble. Where I come from "Campus" is a place where stage-collegians in skull-caps romp around and sing "When Love Is Young in Springtime" in four-part harmony. The reservation in question is known as "the Yard," and I will thank you to call it that in future.)

Anyone who has ever gone back to the old college town after, let us say, ten years, will realize that this country is going to the dogs, especially as regards its youth in the colleges. You get your tickets for the Big Game and you spend a lot of money on railroad fare. (That's all right; you have made a lot of money since getting out. You can afford it.) When you get to the old railroad station you can at least expect that Eddie, the hack driver, will remember you. Eddie, however, is now pretty fat and has five men working for him. You can't even get one of his cabs, much less a nod out of him. O. K. Eddie! The hell with you!

You go to the fraternity house (another concession on my part to my Middle West readers) and announce yourself as "Weekins, 1914." (My class was 1912, as a matter of fact. I am giving myself a slight break and trying to be mysterious about this whole thing.) A lone junior who is hanging around in the front room says, "How do you do? Come on it," and excuses himself immediately. The old place looks about the same, except that an odd-looking banner on the wall says "1930," there being no such year. A couple of young men come in and, seeing you, go right out again. Welcome back to the old House, Weekins!

A couple of young men come in and, seeing you, go right out again.

A steward of some sort enters the room and arranges the magazines on the table.

"Rather quiet for the day of the Big Game," you say to him. "Where is everybody?"

This frightens him and he says, "Thank you, sir!" and also disappears.

Well, after all, you *do* have a certain claim on this place. You helped raise the money for the mission furniture and somewhere up on the wall is a stein with your name on it. There is no reason why you should feel like an intruder. This gives you courage to meet the three young men who enter with books under their arms and pass right by into the hall.

"My name is Weekins, 1914," you say. "Where is everybody?"

"Classes are just over," one of them explains. "Make yourself at home. My name is Hammerbiddle, 1931."

Somehow the mention of such a year as "1931" enrages you. 1931 what? Electrons? But the three young men have gone down the hall, so you will never know.

A familiar face! In between the bead portières comes a man, bald and fat, yet with something about him that strikes an old G chord.

"Billigs!" you cry.

"Stanpfer is the name," he says. "Think of seeing you here!"

You try to make believe that you knew that it was Stanpfer all the time and were just saying Billigs to be funny.

"It must be fifteen years," you say.

"Well, not quite," says Stanpfer, "I saw you two years ago in New York."

"Oh, yes, I know, *that*!" (Where the hell did you see him two years ago? The man is crazy.) "But I mean it must be fifteen years since we were here together."

"Fourteen," he corrects.

"I guess you're right. Fourteen. Well, how the hell are you?"

"Great! How are you?"

"Great! How are you?"

"Great! Couldn't be better. Everything going all right?"

"Great! All right with you?"

"Great! All right with you?"

"You bet."

"That's fine! Kind of quiet around here."

"That's right! Not much like the old days."

"That's right."

"Yes, sir! That's right!"

Perhaps it would be better if the 1931 boys came back. At least, you wouldn't have to recall old days with them. You could start at scratch. Here comes somebody! Somebody older than you, if such a thing is possible.

"Hello," he says, and falls on his face against the edge of the table, cutting his forehead rather badly.

"Up you get!" you say, suiting the action to the word.

"A very nasty turn there," he says, crossly. "They should have that banked."

"That's right," you agree. You remember him as a senior who was particularly snooty to you when you were a sophomore.

"My name is Feemer, 1911," he says, dabbing his forehead with his handkerchief.

"Weekins, 1914," you say.

"Stanpfer, 1914," says Billigs.

"I remember you," says Feemer. "You were an awful pratt."

You give a short laugh.

Feemer begins to sing loudly and hits his head again against the table, this time on purpose. Several of the undergraduates enter and look disapprovingly at all three of you.

By this time Feemer, through constant hitting of his head and lurching about, is slightly ill. The general impression is that you and Stanpfer (or Billigs) are drunk too. These old grads!

The undergraduates (of whom there are now eight or ten) move unpleasantly about the room, rearranging furniture that Feemer has upset and showing in every way at their disposal that they wish you had never come.

"What time is the game?" you ask. You know very well what time the game is.

Nobody answers.

"How are the chances?" Just why you should be making *all* the advances you don't know. After all, you are fourteen years out and these boys could almost be your sons.

"I want everybody here to come to Chicago with me after the game," says Feemer, tying his tie. "I live in Chicago and I want everybody here to come to Chicago with me after the game. I live in Chicago and I want everybody here to come to Chicago with me after the game."

Having made this blanket invitation, Feemer goes to sleep standing up.

The undergraduate disapproval is manifest and includes you and Billigs (or Stanpfer) to such an extent that you might better be at the bottom of the lake.

"How are the chances?" you ask again. "Is Derkwillig going to play?"

"Derkwillig has left college," says one of the undergraduates, scornfully. "He hasn't played since the Penn State game."

"Too bad," you say. "He was good, wasn't he?"

"Not so good."

"I'm sorry. I thought he was, from what I read in the papers."

"The papers are crazy," says a very young man, and immediately leaves the room.

There is a long silence, during which Feemer comes to and looks anxiously into each face as if trying to get his bearings, which is exactly what he is trying to do.

"We might as well clear the room out," says one of the undergraduates. "The girls will be coming pretty soon, and we don't want to have it looking messy."

There is no sign of recognition on either side.

Evidently "looking messy" means the presence of you, Feemer and Stanpfer. This is plain to be seen. So you and Stanpfer each take an arm of Feemer and leave the house. Just as you are going down the steps (a process which includes lurching with Feemer from side to side) you meet Dr. Raddiwell and his wife. There is no sign of recognition on either side.

There is a train leaving town at 1:55. You get it and read about the game in the evening papers.

How I Create

IN AN article on How Authors Create, in which the writing methods of various masters of English prose like Conrad, Shaw, and Barrie are explained (with photographs of them in knickerbockers plaguing dogs and pushing against sun-dials), I discover that I have been doing the whole thing wrong all these years. The interviewer in this case hasn't got around to asking me yet—doubtless because I have been up in my room with the door shut and not answering the bell—but I am going to take a chance, anyway, and tell him how I do my creative work and just how much comes from inspiration and how much from hashish and other perfumes. I may even loosen up and tell him what my favorite hot-weather dishes are.

When I am writing a novel I must actually live the lives of my characters. If, for instance, my hero is a gambler on the French Riviera, I make myself pack up and go to Cannes or Nice, willy-nilly, and there throw myself into the gay life of the gambling set until I really feel that I *am* Paul De Lacroix, Ed Whelan, or whatever my hero's name is. Of course this runs into money, and I am quite likely to have to change my

ideas about my hero entirely and make him a bum on a tramp steamer working his way back to America, or a young college boy out of funds who lives by his wits until his friends at home send him a hundred and ten dollars.

One of my heroes (Dick Markwell in *Love's How-do-you-do*), after starting out as a man about town in New York who "never showed his liquor" and was "an apparently indestructible machine devoted to pleasure," had to be changed into a patient in the Trembly Ward of a local institution, whose old friends didn't recognize him and furthermore didn't want to.

But, as you doubtless remember, it was a corking yarn.

This actually living the lives of my characters takes up quite a lot of time and makes it a little difficult to write anything. It was not until I decided to tell stories about old men who just sit in their rooms and shell walnuts that I ever got around to doing any work. It doesn't make for very interesting novels, but at any rate the wordage is there and there is something to show the publishers for their advance royalties. (Publishers are crotchety that way. They want copy, copy, copy all the time,

Very often I must wait weeks and weeks for what you call "inspiration."

just because they happen to have advanced a measly three hundred dollars a couple of years before. You would think that printing words on paper was their business.)

And now you ask me how I do my work, how my inspiration comes? I will tell you, Little Father. Draw up your chair and let me put my feet on it. Ah, that's better! Now you may go out and play.

Very often I must wait weeks and weeks for what you call "inspiration." In the meantime I must sit with my quill pen poised in air over a sheet of foolscap, in case the divine spark should come like a lightning bolt and knock me off my chair onto my head. (This has happened more than once.) While I am waiting I mull over in my mind what I am going to do with my characters.

Shall I have Mildred marry Lester, or shall Lester marry Evelyn? ("Who is Evelyn?" I often say to myself, never having heard of her before.) Should the French proletariat win the Revolution, or should Louis XVI come back suddenly and establish a Coalition Cabinet? Can I afford to let Etta clean up those dishes in the sink and get them biscuits baked, or would it be better to keep her there for another year, standing first on one foot and then on the other?

You have no idea how many problems an author has to face during those feverish days when he is building a novel, and you have no idea how he solves them. Neither has he.

Sometimes, while in the throes of creative work, I get out of bed in the morning, look at my writing desk piled high with old bills, odd gloves, and empty ginger-ale bottles, and go right back to bed again. The next thing I know it is night once more, and time for the Sand Man to come around. (We have a Sand Man who comes twice a day, which makes it very convenient. We give him five dollars at Christmas.)

Even if I do get up and put on a part of my clothes—I do all my work in a Hawaiian straw skirt and a bow tie of some neutral shade—I often can think of nothing to do but pile the books which are on one end of my desk very neatly on the other end and then kick them one by one off on to the floor with my free foot.

But all the while my brain is work, work, working, and my plot is taking shape. Sometimes it is the shape of a honeydew melon and sometimes a shape which I have never been quite able to figure out. It is a sort of amorphous thing with two heads but no face. When this shape presents itself, I get right back in bed again. I'm no fool.

I find that, while working, a pipe is a great source of inspiration. A pipe can be placed diagonally across the keys of a typewriter so that they will not function, or it can be made to give out such a cloud of smoke that I cannot see the paper. Then, there is the process of lighting it. I can make lighting a pipe a ritual which has not been equaled for elaborateness since the five-day festival to the God of the Harvest. (See my book on Rituals: the Man.)

In the first place, owing to twenty-six years of constant smoking without once calling in a plumber, the space left for tobacco in the bowl of my pipe is now the size of a medium body-pore. Once the match has been applied to the tobacco therein, the smoke is over. This necessitates refilling, relighting, and reknocking. The knocking out of a pipe can be made almost as important as the smoking of it, especially if there are nervous people in the room. A good, smart knock of a pipe against a tin wastebasket and you will have a neurasthenic out of his chair and into the window sash in no time.

The matches, too, have their place in the construction of modern literature. With a pipe like mine, the supply of burnt matches in one day could be floated down the St. Lawrence River with two men jumping them.

When the novel is finished, it is shipped to the Cutting and Binding Room, where native girls roll it into large sheets and stamp on it with their bare feet. This accounts for the funny look of some of my novels. It is then taken back to the Drying Room, where it is rewritten by a boy whom I engage for the purpose, and sent to the publishers. It is then sent back to me.

And so you see now how we creative artists work. It really isn't like any other kind of work, for it must come from a great emotional upheaval in the soul of the writer himself; and if that emotional upheaval is not present, it must come from the work of any other writers which happen to be handy and easily imitated.

The Wreck of the Sunday Paper

WHAT IS to be done with people who can't read a Sunday paper without messing it all up? I just throw this out as one of the problems with which we are faced if we are to keep our civilization from complete collapse.

There is a certain type of citizen (a great many times, I am sorry to have to say, one of the "fair" sex) whose lack of civic pride shows itself in divers forms, but it is in the devastation of a Sunday newspaper that it reaches its full bloom. Show me a Sunday paper which has been left in a condition fit only for kite flying, and I will show you an antisocial and dangerous character who has left it that way.

Such a person may not mean deliberately to do the things to a newspaper that he or (pardon my pointing) *she* does. They really couldn't achieve such colossal disarrangement by any planning or scheming. It has to come from some cataclysmic stroke of a giant force, probably beyond their control. Let them but touch a nice, neat Sunday edition as it lies folded so flat and cold on the doorstep, and immediately the rotogravure section becomes entwined with the sporting section and the editorial page leaps out and joins with the shipping news to form a tent under which a pretty good-sized child could crawl. The society page bundles itself up into a ball in the center of which, by some strange convulsion, the real-estate news conceals itself in a smaller and more compact ball. It is the Touch of Cain that these people have, and perhaps we should not blame them for it.

But they needn't *leave* this mound of rumpled newsprint this way. They could recognize their failing and at least try to correct its ravages before handling the paper on to someone else.

I once knew a man whose wife was a newspaper builder. She built things out of newspapers when she read them. There wasn't much to show for it when she had finished in the way of definite objects; that is, you couldn't quite make out just what she had thought she was building.

But there had very evidently been some very clear idea of making each section of the newspaper into an object of some sort—anything so long as it made the newspaper absolutely unsuited for reading purposes.

Now the man usually tried to get down on Sunday morning ahead of his wife so that he could have first crack at the paper before the Great Disintegration set it. But, owing to a habit he had formed in his youth of staying out late on Saturday nights, he found it difficult to beat her to it. By the time he got downstairs the room looked like a militia encampment.

"What do you do with a newspaper?" he once asked her, as quietly as he could. "Try to dress yourself in it? You'll never get anywhere without buttons, you know."

But she didn't seem to mind his taunts, and, in fact, more or less put him on the defensive by calling him "an old maid"; so he decided that the time had come for action. He ordered *two* editions of each Sunday paper, one for his wife to mux about with and one for himself.

It was then that he discovered that his helpmeet's rolling herself up in the paper was not just an unconscious weakness on her part but a vicious perversion from which she got a fiendish pleasure. She would sneak upstairs and get his personal edition before he was awake and give it the works, pretending that she couldn't find her own.

She was simply doing it to be mean, that was all. Often her own copy would be untouched and he would find it on Monday morning hidden away behind the sofa in its pristine smoothness.

I suppose, in a way, that the inability to read a newspaper which someone else has wrapped around himself or which is in any way disarranged is a sign of abnormality in itself and that we sensitive ones are in the wrong. All right, then—*I'm* the one to blame. *I'm* the enemy to society and the one to be locked up. But the fact remains that I am going to stand just so much more of this thing and then away *some*body goes to the police station.

The Real Public Enemies

I HAVE now reached an age when I feel that I am pretty well able to take care of myself against animate enemies. By "animate enemies" I mean living people, like burglars, drunks, or police—people who set out with a definite idea in their minds of getting me. Mind you, I don't mean that I can lick these people in a hand-to-hand encounter, but I do know, in a general way, what to do when they attack me, even if it is only to run.

It is the inanimate enemies who have me baffled. The hundred and one little bits of wood and metal that go to make up the impedimenta of our daily life—the shoes and pins, the picture books and door keys, the bits of fluff and sheets of newspaper—each and every one with just as much vicious ill-will toward me personally as the meanest footpad who roams the streets, each and every one bent on my humiliation and working together, as on one great team, to bedevil and confuse me and to get me into a neurasthenics' home before I am sixty. I can't fight these boys. They've got me licked.

When I was very young and first realized the conspiracy against me on the part of these inanimate things, I had a boyish idea that force was the thing to use. When a shoestring had clearly shown that it was definitely *not* going to be put through the eyelet, I would give it a yank that broke it in two, and feel that the bother of getting a new lace was not too much to pay for the physical pain which the old lace must have suffered. In fact, as I put in the new one I had an idea that it was pretty well frightened at the example of its predecessor and would jolly well behave itself or suffer the same fate.

But after years of getting out new laces and buying new fountain pens (my method, when a pen refused to work, was to press down on it so hard that the points spread open like a fork and then to rip the paper in a frenzied imitation of writing), I gradually realized that I was being the sucker in the battle and that the use of force didn't pay in the long run.

I then started trying subtlety. If there is one field in fighting in which a human ought to be able to win out over a piece of wood, it is in tricky maneuvering. Take, for example, when you are trying to read a newspaper on top of a bus. We will start with the premise that the newspaper knows what you are trying to do and has already made up its mind that you are not going to do it. Very well, Mr. Newspaper, we'll see! (Later on you don't call it "Mr. Newspaper." You call it "you —— ——!" But that is after you know it better.)

Suppose you want to open it to page four. The thing to do is not to hold it up and try to turn it as you would an ordinary newspaper. If you do, it will turn into a full-rigged brigantine, each sheet forming a sail, and will crash head-on into your face, blinding you and sometimes carrying you right off the bus.

The best way is to say, as if talking to yourself, "Well, I guess I'll turn to page seven." Or better yet, let the paper overhear you say, "Oh, well, I guess I won't read any more," and make a move as if to put it away in your pocket. Then, quick as a wink, give it a quick turn inside out before it realizes what is happening.

It won't take it long to catch on, but, thinking that you want to turn to page seven, as you said, it will quite possibly open to page four, which was the one you wanted.

But even this system of *sotto voce* talking and deceit does not always work. In the first place, you have to have a pretty young newspaper, who hasn't had much experience, for all the older ones will be on to your game and will play it back at you for all it is worth.

The only way to be safe about the thing is to take it all very calmly and try to do your best with deliberate fierceness, folding each page over under your feet very slowly until you come to the right one. But by that time you have got the paper in such a condition that it cannot be read—so you lose anyway.

Of course, after years of antagonizing members of the inanimate underworld, you are going to get an active conspiracy against you, with physical violence on *their* part as its aim. It then becomes, not an aggressive campaign on your part, but one of defense to save yourself from being attacked.

For example, I have a pair of military brushes which have definitely signed up to put me on the spot and will, I am afraid, ultimately kill me. I have taken those brushes from the bureau and held them in a position to brush my hair, without an unkind thought in my mind, and have had them actually fly out of my hands, execute a pretty take-off of perhaps a foot and a half, and then crash into my forehead with as deft a "one-two" as any heavyweight ever pulled on a groggy opponent.

I have placed slippers very carefully under my bed, only to have them crawl out during the night to a position where I will step into them the wrong way round when leaping out of bed to answer the telephone.

These things don't just happen, you know. They are proofs of a very clear conspiracy to hurt me physically which exists among household objects, and against which I have no defense. All that I can do is to walk about all day crouched over with one elbow raised to ward off the heavier attacks which are being aimed at me. This gives a man a cringing look which so becomes a personal characteristic.

It is this element of physical danger which has entered my struggle with these things which has got me worried. I will match myself in an unequal fight to open a can of sardines or a bottle of water, if the issue is to be merely whether I get it open or not. But I can't face the inevitable gashing and bleeding which always follow my failure. I will tackle the closing of a trunk or suitcase, but I am already licked by the knowledge that, no matter how the fight turns out, the metal snaps are going to reach out and nip my fingers.

The only thing that I can do, as old age and experience bear down on me, is to sit with my hands in my pockets and try nothing.

I have said that, in my youth, I gave up the use of force when little things thwarted me. I *should* have given it up, but there is one enemy which I still lash out at in futile bludgeonings. It is the typewriter on which I am writing this article. In putting on a ribbon I lose myself entirely, and invariably end up completely festooned like Laocoön, ripping and tearing madly with ink-stained fingers at a ribbon which long before I had rendered useless. I am also thrown into raging fits of physical violence when, owing to some technical fault which I do not understand, the letters begin getting dimmer and dimmer, finally becoming just shells of their natural selves. On such occasions I start very quietly hitting the keys harder and harder, muttering, "Oh, you won't, won't you?" until I am crashing down with both fists on the keyboard and screaming, "Take that—and *that*!"

In fact, as I write this, I detect a weakening in the pigment of the ribbon, and, as I strike each key, less and less seems to be happening. I will try to be calm.

I must try to remember that it does no good to inflict pain on inanimate things and that the best that I can do is break the typewriter . . . but really . . . after all . . . you xxxxx you xxxxxxxxxxxx take that xxxxxxxxxxxxx and *that* xxxxxxxxxxxx.

Johnny-on-the-Spot

IF YOU want to get a good perspective on history in the making, just skim through a collection of news photographs which have been snapped at those very moments when cataclysmic events were taking place throughout the world. In almost every picture you can discover one guy in a derby hat who is looking in exactly the opposite direction from the excitement, totally oblivious to the fact that the world is shaking beneath his feet. That would be me, or at any rate, my agent in that particular part of the world in which the event is taking place.

I have not seen an actual photograph of the shooting of the Austrian Archduke at Sarajevo, but I would be willing to bet, if one is in existence, that you could find, somewhere off in the right foreground, a man in a Serbian derby looking anxiously up the street for a trolley car. And probably right up in the foreground a youth smiling and waving into the camera.

Revolutionary disturbances are particularly subject to this blasé treatment on the part of bystanders. Photographs which have come up from Cuba lately, and even those of the wildest days in Russia during the Reign of Terror—photographs taken at the risk of the lives of the photographers themselves—all show, somewhere in their composition, an area of complete calm in which at least one man is looking at his watch or picking his teeth.

And I shall probably be wearing a derby.

In one which I have before me from Havana we see crowds of people fleeing before machine-gun bullets, soldiers dashing hither and yon with uplifted sabres, puffs of smoke stippling the background, and down in one corner, by a news kiosk, a man in his shirtsleeves looking up at a clock.

At any rate, there'll be one guy who knows what time the trouble started—provided he knew that it *had* started.

Are these men in derby hats really men of iron, who take revolutions and assassinations in their stride as all part of the day's work, or are they hard of hearing, or near-sighted, or, possibly, are they just men who go through life missing things?

I like to think of them as in the third category, for I know that if I were on the spot during any important historical event I would not know about it until I read the papers the next day. I am unobservant to the point of being what scientists might call "half-witted." It isn't that I don't see things, but that I don't register them. This is what makes it so difficult for me in traffic.

I could have worked in a shop in the Place de la Bastille, or have sold papers across from the Old State House in Boston, or have been an usher in Ford's Theatre in Washington, and yet would probably have noticed nothing of the events for which those spots are famous. I possibly might have been aware of a slight commotion and, if I had worked in Ford's Theatre, wondered why the curtain was rung down so early; but, on going home, I would have been pretty sure to report a routine evening to the family. "They didn't finish *Our American Cousin* to-night," I might have said. "Some trouble with the lights, I guess."

All this makes for a calm, well-ordered existence, with practically no nerve strain. Those men in derbies and I, provided we do not get hit by stray bullets, ought to live to a ripe old age if we take any kind of care of our kidneys at all. Dynasties may fall, cities may collapse, and the world be brought down about our ears, but, unless something hits us squarely in the back, we are sitting pretty.

I do rather dread the day, however, when I look at a photograph of the focal point of the World Revolution and see myself smirking into the camera with my back to the fighting. And the worst of it will be that I shall probably be wearing a derby.

Down with Pigeons

ST. FRANCIS OF ASSISI (unless I am getting him mixed up with St. Simeon Stylites, which might be very easy to do as both their names begin with "St.") was very fond of birds, and often had his picture taken with them sitting on his shoulders and pecking at his wrists. That was all right, if St. Francis liked it. We all have our likes and dislikes, and I have more of a feeling for dogs. However, I am not *against* birds as a class. I am just against pigeons.

I do not consider pigeons birds, in the first place. They are more in the nature of people; people who mooch. Probably my feeling about pigeons arises from the fact that all my life I have lived in rooms where pigeons came rumbling in and out of my window. I myself must have a certain morbid fascination for pigeons, because they follow me about so much—and with evident ill-will. I am firmly convinced that they are trying to haunt me.

Although I live in the middle of a very large city (well, to show you how large it is—it is the largest in the world) I am awakened every

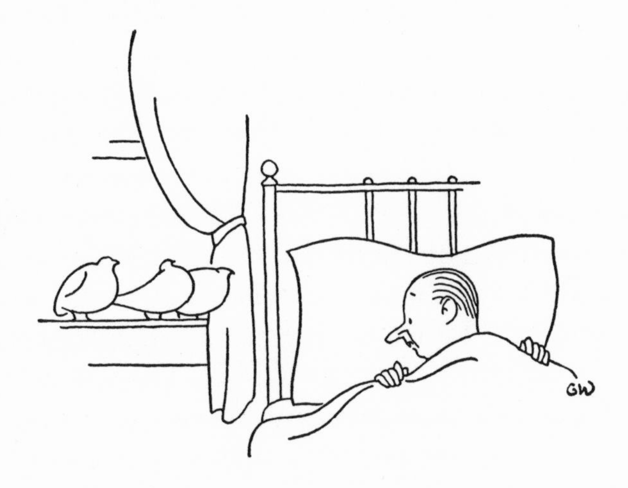

Pigeons walking in at my window and sneering at me.

morning by a low gargling sound which turns out to be the result of one, or two, or three pigeons walking in at my window and sneering at me. Granted that I am a fit subject for sneering as I lie there, possibly with one shoe on or an unattractive expression on my face, but there is something more than just a passing criticism in these birds making remarks about me. They have some ugly scheme on foot against me, and I know it. Sooner or later it will come out, and then I can sue.

This thing has been going on ever since I was in college. In our college everybody was very proud of the pigeons. Anyone walking across the Yard (Campus to you, please) was beset by large birds who insisted on climbing up his waistcoat and looking about in his wallet for nuts or raisins or whatever it is you feed pigeons (bichloride would be my suggestion, but let it pass).

God knows that I was decent enough to them in my undergraduate days. I let them walk up and down my back and I tried to be as nice as I could without actually letting them see that I was not so crazy about it. I even gave them chestnuts, chestnuts which I wanted myself. I now regret my generosity, for good chestnuts are hard to get these days.

But somehow the word got around in pigeon circles that Benchley was antipigeon. They began pestering me. I would go to bed at night, tired from overstudy, and at six-thirty in the morning the Big Parade would begin. The line of march was as follows: Light on Benchley's window sill, march once in through the open window, going "Grumble-grumble-grumble" in a sinister tone. Then out and stand on the sill, urging other pigeons to come in and take a crack at it.

There is very little fun in waking up with a headache and hearing an ominous murmuring noise, with just the suggestion of a passing shadow moving across your window sill. No man should be asked to submit to this *all* his life.

I once went to Venice (Italy), and there, with the rest of the tourists, stood in awe in the center of St. Mark's Piazza, gazing at the stately portals of the church and at the lovely green drinks served at Florian's for those who don't want to look at the church all of the time.

It is an age-old custom for tourists to feed corn to the pigeons and then for the pigeons to crawl all over the tourists. This has been going on without interruption ever since Americans discovered Venice. So far as the records show, no pigeon has ever failed a tourist—and no tourist has ever failed a pigeon. It is a very pretty relationship.

I tried to be as nice as I could.

In my case, however, it was different. In the first place, the St. Mark's pigeons, having received word from the American chapter of their lodge, began flying at me in such numbers and with such force as actually to endanger my life. They came in great droves, all flying low and hard, just barely skimming my hat and whirring in an ugly fashion with some idea of intimidating me. But by that time I was not to be intimidated, and, although I ducked very low and lost my hat several times, I did not give in. I even bought some corn from one of the vendors and held it out in my hand, albeit with bad grace. But, for the first time in centuries, no pigeon fell for the corn gag. I stood alone in the middle of St. Mark's Square, holding out my hand dripping with kernels of golden corn, and was openly and deliberately snubbed. One or two of the creatures walked up to within about ten feet of me and gave me a nasty look, but not one gave my corn a tumble. So I decided the hell with them and ate the corn myself.

Now this sort of thing must be the result of a very definite boycott, or, in its more aggressive stage, an anti-Benchley campaign. Left to myself, I would have only the very friendliest feelings for pigeons (it is too late now, but I might once have been won over). But having been put on my mettle, there is nothing that I can do now but fight back. Whatever I may be, I am not yellow.

Here is my plan. I know that I am alone in this fight, for most people like pigeons, or, at any rate, are not antagonized by them. But single-handed I will take up the cudgels, and I hope that, when they grow up, my boys will carry on the battle on every cornice and every campus in the land.

Whenever I meet a pigeon, whether it be on my own window sill or walking across a public park, I will stop still and place my hands on my hips and wait. If the pigeon wants to make the first move and attack me, I will definitely strike back, even to the extent of hitting it with my open palm and knocking it senseless (not a very difficult feat, I should think, as they seem to have very little sense).

If they prefer to fight it out by innuendo and sneering, I will fight it out by innuendo and sneering. I have worked up a noise which I can make in my throat which is just as unpleasant sounding as theirs. I will even take advantage of my God-given power of speech and will say, "Well, what do you want to make of it, you waddling, cooing so-and-sos?" I will glare at them just as they glare at me, and if they come within reach of my foot, so help me, St. Francis, I will kick at them. *And* the next pigeon that strolls in across my window ledge when I am just awakening, I will catch with an especially prepared trap and will drag into my room, there to punch the living daylights out of him.

I know that this sounds very cruel and very much as if I were an animal hater. As a matter of fact, I am such a friend of animals in general that I am practically penniless. I have been known to take in dogs who were obviously impostors and put them through college. I am a sucker for kittens, even though I know that one day they will grow into cats who will betray and traduce me. I have even been known to pat a tiger cub, which accounts for my writing this article with my left hand.

But as far as pigeons go, I am through. It is a war to the death, and I have a horrible feeling that the pigeons are going to win.

Ladies Wild

IN THE exclusive set (no diphtheria cases allowed) in which I travel, I am known as a heel in the matter of parlor games. I will drink with them, wrassle with them and, now and again, leer at the ladies, but when they bring out the bundles of pencils and the pads of paper and start putting down all the things they can think of beginning with "W," or enumerating each other's bad qualities on a scale of 100 (no hard-feeling results, mind you—just life-long enmity), I tip-toe noisily out of the room and say, "The hell with you."

For this reason, I am not usually included in any little games that may be planned in advance. If they foresee an evening of "Consequences" coming over them, they whisper "Get Benchley out of the house. Get him a horse to ride, or some beads to string—anything to get him out of the way." For, I forgot to tell you, not only am I a non-participant in parlor games, but I am a militant non-participant. I heckle from the sidelines. I throw stones and spit at the players. Hence the nickname "Sweet Old Bob," or sometimes just the initials.

One night last summer, I detected, from the general stir among the ladies and more effete gents, that I was being eased out of the house. This meant that the gaming was about to begin. But instead of the usual clatter of pencils among the *croupiers,* I saw someone sneaking in with a tray of poker chips. They almost had me out the door when I discovered what was up.

"Well, so long, Bob," they said. "Good bowling to you."

"What's this?" I came back into the room. "Are those poker chips?"

"Sure, they're poker chips. It's all right to play poker, isn't it? The reform administration's gone out."

I assumed a hurt air. In fact, I didn't have to assume it. I was hurt.

"I don't suppose I'm good enough to play poker with you," I said. "All I'm good enough for is to furnish the liquor and the dancing girls."

"Why, we thought you didn't like games. You always act like such a goddamned heel whenever a game is suggested."

"My dear people," I said, trying to be calm, "there are games and games. 'Twenty Questions' is one game, if you will, but poker—why, poker is a man's game. It's my dish. I'm an old newspaperman, you know. Poker is the breath of life to a newspaperman." (As a matter of fact, I never played poker once when I was on a newspaper, and was never allowed to do more than kibitz at the Thanatopsis games of Broun, Adams, Kaufman, and that bunch, but poker is still my favorite game in a small way, or at least it *was.*)

Then there was a great scrambling to get me a chair, and sell me chips. "Old Bob's going to play!" was the cry. "Old Bob likes poker!" People came in from the next room to see what the commotion was, and one woman said that, if I was going to play, she had a headache. (I had ruined a game of "Who Am I?" for her once by blowing out a fuse from the coat-closet.)

As for me, I acted the part to the hilt. I took off my coat, unbuttoned my vest so that just the watch-chain connected it, lighted my pipe, and kept my hat on the back of my head.

"This is the real poker costume," I said. "The way we used to play it down on the old Trib. There ought to be a City News ticker over in the corner to make it seem like home."

"This is the real poker costume," I said.

"I'm afraid he's going to be too good for us," said one of the more timid ladies. "We play for very small stakes, you know."

"The money doesn't matter," I laughed. "It's the game. And anyway," I added modestly, "I haven't played for a long time. You'll probably take me good." (I wish now that I had made book on that prediction.)

It was to be Dealer's Choice, which should have given me a tip-off right there, with three women at the table, one the dealer.

"This," she announced, looking up into space as if for inspiration, "is going to be 'Hay Fever.' "

"I beg pardon," I said, leaning forward.

" 'Hay Fever,' " explained one of the men. "The girls like it. One card up, two down, the last two up. One-eyed Jacks, sevens, and nines wild. High-low."

"I thought this was going to be poker," I said.

"From then on you play it just like regular poker," said the dealer.

From then on! My God! Just like regular poker!

Having established myself as an old poker-fan, I didn't want to break down and cry at the very start, so I played the hand through. I say I "played" it. I sat looking at my cards, peeking now and then just to throw a bluff that I knew what I was doing. One-eyed Jacks, sevens, and nines wild, I kept saying that to myself, and puffing very hard at my pipe. After a minute of owlish deliberation, I folded.

The next hand was to be "Whistle Up Your Windpipe," another one which the girls had introduced into the group and which the men, weak-kneed sissies that they were, had allowed to become regulation. This was seven-card stud, first and last cards up, deuces, treys, and red-haired Queens wild, high-low-and-medium. I figured out that I had a very nice straight, bet it as I would have bet a straight in the old days, and was beaten to eleven dollars and sixty cents by a royal straight flush. Amid general laughter, I was told that an ordinary straight in these games is worth no more than a pair of sixes in regular poker. A royal straight flush usually wins. Well, it usually won in the old days, too.

By the time the deal came to me, my pipe had gone out and I had taken my hat off. Between clenched teeth I announced, "And this, my frands, is going to be something *you* may not have heard of. This is going to be *old-fashioned draw-poker,* with *nothing* wild." The women had to have it explained to them, and remarked that they didn't see much fun in that. However, the hand was played. Nobody had anything (in comparison to what they had been having in the boom days), and nobody bet. The hand was over in a minute and a half, amid terrific silence.

That was the chief horror of this epidemic of "Whistle Up Your Windpipe," "Beezy-Weezy," and "Mice Afloat." It made old-fashioned stud seem tame, even to me. Every time it came to me, I elected the old game, just out of spite, but nobody's heart was in it. I became the spoil-sport of the party again, and once or twice I caught them trying to slip the deal past me, as if by mistake. Even a round of jackpots netted nothing in the way of excitement, and even when I won one on a full house, there was no savour to the victory, as I had to explain to the women what a full house was. They thought that I was making up my own rules. Nothing as small as a full house had ever been seen in that game.

The Big Newspaper Man was taken for exactly sixty-one dollars and eight cents when the game broke up at four A.M. Two of the women were the big winners. They had finally got it down to a game where everything was wild but the black nines, and everyone was trying for "low."

From now on I not only walk out on "Twenty Questions" and "Who Am I?" but, when there are ladies present (God *bless* them!), I walk out on poker. And a fine state of affairs it is when an old newspaperman has to walk out on poker!

My Face

MERELY AS an observer of natural phenomena, I am fascinated by my own personal appearance. This does not mean that I am *pleased* with it, mind you, or that I can even tolerate it. I simply have a morbid interest in it.

Each day I look like someone, or some*thing*, different. I never know what it is going to be until I steal a look in the glass. (Oh, I don't suppose you really could call it stealing. It belongs to me, after all.)

One day I look like Wimpy, the hamburger fancier in the Popeye

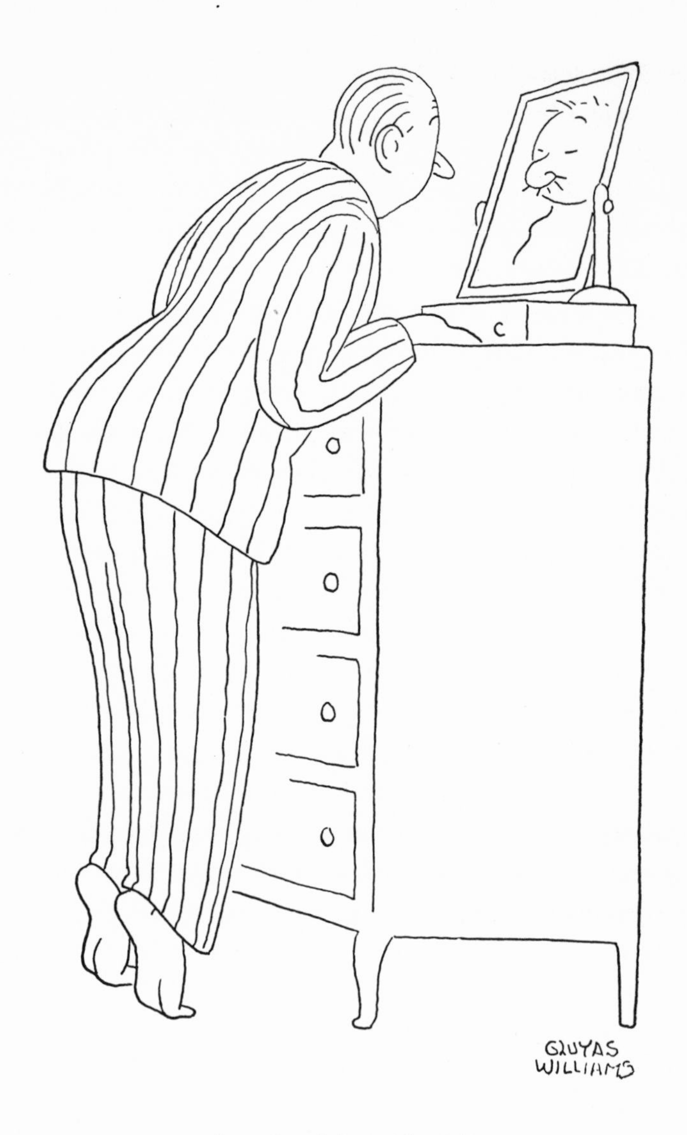

One day I look like Wimpy.

the Sailor saga. Another day it may be Wallace Beery. And a third day, if I have let my mustache get out of hand, it is Bairnsfather's Old Bill. And not until I peek do I know what the show is going to be.

Some mornings, if I look in the mirror soon enough after getting out of bed, there is no resemblance to any character at all, either in or out of fiction, and I turn quickly to look behind me, convinced that a stranger has spent the night with me and is peering over my shoulder in a sinister fashion, merely to frighten me. On such occasions, the shock of finding that I am actually possessor of the face in the mirror is sufficient to send me scurrying back to bed, completely unnerved.

All this is, of course, very depressing, and I often give off a low moan at the sight of the new day's metamorphosis, but I can't seem to resist the temptation to learn the worst. I even go out of my way to look at myself in store-window mirrors, just to see how long it will take me to recognize myself. If I happen to have on a new hat, or am walking with a limp, I sometimes pass right by my reflection without even nodding. Then I begin to think: "You must have given off *some* visual impression into that mirror. You're not a disembodied spirit yet—I hope."

And I go back and look again, and, sure enough, the strange-looking man I thought was walking just ahead of me in the reflection turns out to have been my own image all the time. It makes a fellow stop and think, I can tell you.

This almost masochistic craving to offend my own aesthetic sense by looking at myself and wincing also comes out when snapshots or class photographs are being passed around. The minute someone brings the envelope containing the week's grist of vacation prints from the drugstore developing plant, I can hardly wait to get my hands on them. I try to dissemble my eagerness to examine those in which I myself figure, but there is a greedy look in my eye which must give me away.

The snapshots in which I do not appear are so much dross in my eyes, but I pretend that I am equally interested in them all.

"This is very good of Joe," I say, with a hollow ring to my voice, sneaking a look at the next print to see if I am in it.

Ah! Here, at last, is one in which I show up nicely. By "nicely" I mean "clearly." Try as I will to pass it by casually, my eyes rivet themselves on that corner of the group in which I am standing. And then, when the others have left the room, I surreptitiously go through the envelope again, just to gaze my fill on the slightly macabre sight of Myself as others see me.

In some pictures I look even worse than I had imagined. On what I call my "good days," I string along pretty close to form. But day in and day out, in mirror or in photograph, there is always that slight shock of surprise which, although unpleasant, lends a tang to the adventure of peeking. I never can quite make it seem possible that this is really Poor Little Me, the Little Me I know so well and yet who frightens me so when face to face.

My only hope is that, in this constant metamorphosis which seems to be going on, a winning number may come up sometime, if only for a day. Just what the final outcome will be, it is hard to predict. I may settle down to a constant, plodding replica of Man Mountain Dean in my old age, or change my style completely and end up as a series of Bulgarian peasant types. I may just grow old along with Wimpy.

But whatever is in store for me, I shall watch the daily modulations with an impersonal fascination not unmixed with awe at Mother Nature's gift for caricature, and will take the bitter with the sweet and keep a stiff upper lip.

As a matter of fact, my upper lip is pretty fascinating by itself, in a bizarre sort of way.

Why I Am Pale

ONE OF THE reasons (in case you give a darn) for that unreasonable pallor of mine in mid-Summer, is that I can seem to find no comfortable position in which to lie in the sun. A couple of minutes on my elbows, a couple of minutes on my back, and then the cramping sets in and I have to scramble to my feet. And you can't get very tanned in four minutes.

I see other people, especially women (who must be made of rubber), taking books to the beach or up on the roof for a whole day of lolling about in the sun in various attitudes of relaxation, hardly moving from one position over a period of hours. I have even tried it myself.

But after arranging myself in what I take, for the moment, to be a comfortable posture, with vast areas of my skin exposed to the actinic rays and the book in a shadow so that I do not blind myself, I find that my elbows are beginning to dig their way into the sand, or that they are acquiring "sheet-burns" from the mattress; that the small of my back is sinking in as far as my abdomen will allow, and that both knees are bending backward, with considerable tugging at the ligaments.

This is obviously not the way for me to lie. So I roll over on my back, holding the book up in the air between my eyes and the sun. I am not even deluding myself by this maneuver. I know that it won't work for long. So, as soon as paralysis of the arms sets in, I drop the book on my chest (without having read more than three consecutive words), thinking that perhaps I may catch a little doze.

But sun shining on closed eyelids (on *my* closed eyelids) soon induces large purple azaleas whirling against a yellow background, and the sand at the back of my neck starts crawling. (I can be stark naked and still have something at the back of my neck for sand to get in under.) So it is a matter of perhaps a minute and a half before I am over on my stomach again with a grunt, this time with the sand in my lips.

There are several positions in which I may arrange my arms, all of them wrong. Under my head, to keep the sand or mattress out of my mouth; down straight at my sides, or stretched out like a cross; no mat-

Often I have to be assisted to my feet.

ter which, they soon develop unmistakable symptoms of arthritis and have to be shifted, also with grunting.

Lying on one hip, with one elbow supporting the head, is no better, as both joints soon start swelling and aching, with every indication of becoming infected, and often I have to be assisted to my feet from this position.

Once on my feet, I try to bask standing up in various postures, but this results only in a sunburn on the top of my forehead and the entire surface of my nose, with occasional painful blisters on the tops of my shoulders. So gradually, trying to look as if I were just ambling aimlessly about, I edge my way toward the clubhouse, where a good comfortable chair and a long cooling drink soon put an end to all this monkey-business.

I am afraid that I am more the pale type, and should definitely give up trying to look rugged.

Men of Harlech!

In certain moods I love to lapse into song, loud and fairly clear.

IT IS TOO late to do anything about it now, but I sometimes wish that my paternal ancestors had not been Welsh. I can't seem to get the hang of Welsh songs.

In certain moods, I love to lapse into song, loud and fairly clear (clear enough, I am told), and, under such conditions, it is more fitting if one can sing the songs of one's own race. It makes it easier to get to crying.

But I don't know any Welsh songs, and even if I did, I couldn't sing them. We never spoke Welsh at home for some reason, possibly because my maternal stock was Scotch-Irish. We compromised on a rather flat New England dialect, containing practically no romantic implications, and I have inherited no folk-songs from that quarter either.

The Welsh are great singers, I am told, which makes it all the more tantalizing. It would be nice if I could, when the lust for singing comes

It would be nice if I could go into a Welsh miners' chorus.

over me, settle back and go into a Welsh miners' chorus, so that people would nudge each other and whisper, "His people were Welsh, you know. It's practically a folk-song with him!" That's the way to sing, my lads! Sing the songs that are in your blood!

But what am I to do about Welsh songs? Mr. J. B. Morton, in the *London Express,* has reconstructed, or improvised, a Welsh song for us, which will give you some idea of what I am up against in my sentimental, nostalgic moments. I quote from memory and, therefore, I am afraid, sketchily:

WELSH SONG

Wirion digon gul noch noch
With a hey down derry and a ddwpllwdpoch
Ei gsith och deb nam rydidd gam
With a hey derry di-do caethion pam.
Llewsithery fwll ned dinam cnu
Gwerthyr yw brenin myy fansth
Sing hey for the nhaith meddyn ddica gstrth.

(*Note to linotyper:* I'm terribly sorry about putting you to all that trouble. As a matter of fact I left out one line just to make it a little easier for you and, as a result, shall probably be deluged with letters from angry Welshmen, *R. B.*)

But you see how I am fixed when it comes time to lapse into songs of the Home Land. I don't even know any Ulster songs. So the result is that when I feel a spell of loud singing coming on I go German, and no one is more surprised than the Germans.

So far as I know, and so far as anyone can tell who has heard me sing German, I have not a drop of German blood in me. But in a rather pathetic attempt to find some *Heimat* songs that I can sing I give myself, body and soul, to the Rhineland, although, to be specific, I am more inclined toward Austria as my adopted song-country. Austria or Bavaria. I think that really I am more Bavarian than anything when I get to singing.

This sort of thing could make for internationalism, if carried far enough, so I will say no more about it. But the whole thing could have been avoided if the Welsh had written songs that I could sing.

X.

The Writing Public

By GLUYAS WILLIAMS

With Captions by Russell Maloney

"Dear Mary:—I'll bet you don't remember the man with the crew haircut that stayed with Ted Fitz last Labor Day weekend, but if you do you will remember that you said you bet I wouldn't remember to write, and I bet I would remember, because I had a better time at the Country Club dance th any other dance I ever was at. Well, in only ele months I will be off to Yale, and I wonder if will remember what I said when you said what said about Yale men . . ."

'Dear Fred:—Saw you folks going out to · movies tonight, and just thought I'd slip ıote under your door before I forgot. Just nted to say that it's been a long time since had a game of bridge with you folks. We must try to get together soon. By the way, just happened to notice this morning that your dog has been digging in our flower beds. No great harm done, of course, but we were just wondering if . . ."

"Gentlemen:—I don't suppose the opinion of one who climbs into a sixty-five-cent upper gallery seat carries quite as much weight as the wishes of the ermine-wrapped patrons who adorn the boxes. But when we keep getting the D Minor, the Lovedeath and such hackneyed fare from week to week, to the total exclusion of contemporary artists, then I se appeasement has gone too far. I wouldn't expect t find you programming Schönberg and Bartók (!, but in the name of heaven, have we become so oss fied that not even a little Mahler, Prokofieff o even . . ."

Dear Miss Snell:—I am sure that Danny is very that he put paste in the little girl's hair. It just high spirits, of course, but he should be made to realize that it's naughty. I am sure that Danny has 'learned his lesson,' but if he ever does it again, I hope you will . . ."

"Mr. Chman, fellow membrs—more used to working than talking about—but have message—like little grl our nborhood asked why didn't like to go Sunday sch—but seriously want to impress 3 facts—1. Need for co-operation—everybody pull together.—2.
enterprise—as old night watchman said when me working late at office—nobody going tell us run business . . ."

XI.

FROM

There's a Fly in This Room!

AND

Wrap It as a Gift

By RALF KIRCHER

"There's a Fly in This Room!"

HISTORIANS say that history repeats itself and scientists say that everything moves in cycles. Call it history you historians, call it cycles you scientists, call it evolution you monkeys—the fact remains that a man spends most of his time feeling that this is where he came in. Putting up the screens every year is just one more proof that life is a squirrel cage from which alas! there is no escape. On top of that, nobody has thrown me a nut since goodness knows when.

Mind you, I do not pretend to speak for other men who may, for all I know, prefer to maintain a disgusted silence on this subject, but I will speak for myself and what I will say for myself is this: I am getting tired of that old nightmare called "Putting Up the Screens." If there are others of you who share these sentiments, meet me at the Fairgrounds next Saturday morning at ten, where we will form ranks of four and march down Elm Street to Walnut, south on Walnut to Main, and west on Main to the courthouse where we will demonstrate, burn effigies, and make speeches on the lawn until beaten off by the police. This will do no good but it will be a change.

The husband doesn't live, or at least I wouldn't call it living, who would ever put up a screen of his own free will. By the same token, or unreasonable facsimile thereof, the woman doesn't live who will give a man a moment's peace until he does. Sometimes it begins as early as March.

"There's a fly in this room!" she will shriek, employing the anguish used by the heroine who discovers that she is not alone in the haunted tower, having been joined by a wispy visitor who died of stab-wounds in 1734. Ghosts, cobras, black widow spiders, and insurance agents are welcome guests compared to the first fly.

"We will have to put up the screens," she says firmly, using the editorial "we" which in this case means you.

You do not see this fly yourself and furthermore you do not even

hear it, but you soon grow acquainted with its character as, night after night, you are told how it has been lunging about from room to room all day, stealing food from the refrigerator, scaring the baby, knocking over vases, insulting the milkman, and making a nuisance of itself in other ways that are apparent to a woman but never observed by a man. And each of these shrill recitals is concluded with the observation that we simply must put up the screens. Soon you conclude that, in the hell-hath-no-fury department, the woman whose screens are down has it all over the woman scorned. But with one artful dodge and another you manage to put it off because you remember what happened the last time you put up the screens. Anyone who has fallen out of a second-story window and landed in the barberry with his head through a screen will not need to be reminded that the whole thing is an ugly business. Am I right, chum?

But you'll not put it off forever because, as Spring wears on, more flies and assorted insects put in their appearance and these so increase the threats and laments that you are driven to the job willy-nilly, whatever that means. Willy Nilly, incidentally, would be an appropriate name for a guy who likes to put up screens.

Some day an architect is going to make a fortune by designing a house with at least two windows the same size because that will greatly simplify the screen-hanging problem and men will not only buy that architect's houses like wild cakes but will also erect a monument to him in the public square. Up to now, however, no house has been built with two windows that are exactly the same size. This means that no two screens are alike, which means that with forty-three different windows and forty-three different screens you can try to put the wrong screen in the wrong window 1849 times. Incidentally, speaking of 1849, Polk was president then, but that's probably beside the point. Thus, with all this opportunity for error you will have to develop a system or quit work and devote full time to the job. So you use a system, laying all the screens out on the lawn and then skittering around the house trying to match the right screens to the right windows. In maybe an hour you have screens scattered all over the property, inside and out. It is at this point that you are approached by the originator of all this trouble who reminds you that the screens have to be washed first, stupid. By this time you are a defeated man anyway so you merely knuckle your forehead and mutter, "Yas'um, Missie Lagree," and shuffle off like a faithful old family retainer to collect the screens and squirt them with the hose.

Dusk is settling over the neighborhood when the screens are finally hung and you lower yourself slowly into the steamer chair on the porch. It is a quiet, peaceful evening. Leaves rustle softly in the twilight breeze. A boy in the next block is torturing a clarinet. Lights flick on like lights in the windows across the way.

A shadow moves from the doorway and settles softly on the glider.

"Now, really, was it such a dreadful job?" she asks gently.

You slouch deeper in the chair and listen for a moment to the quiet of the night.

"A plague," you say. "A plague on flies and on architects and on screens. A plague on October when I'll have to take them down. And a plague apiece on history and on cycles, too."

She smiles to herself but doesn't speak, for you are fast asleep.

"Giddap! Daddy!"

THERE COMES a day in every man's life when he begins to look silly in a stocking cap. My day was last Saturday.

We had a nice fall of snow last Saturday, and if there is anything that will bring out the colt in a man it is a nice fall of snow, particularly if he is a little giddy as a general thing, and particularly if he lives in the vicinity of a hill and has a son who owns a sled. Given this nasty set of circumstances, he will begin to dream about his boyhood and will hang around the water cooler all Saturday morning telling the Assistant Purchasing Agent how he used to go down Dead Man's Hill standing up on his sled—standing up, mind you! Regular daredevil he was, and folks said his parents would never raise that boy—swore he'd kill himself! But don't you believe it! It took more than Dead Man's Hill to scare him when he was a boy! Why, he remembers the time, remembers it like it was only yesterday, when there was a nice fall of snow just about like the one we have today, only a little deeper, and right after school—but by this time the Assistant Purchasing Agent has backed out of earshot. That doesn't make any difference however, because by now the damage is done.

A bright spot of color is glowing in each sallow cheek as our hero bursts into the front room that afternoon and announces, in what he believes is a hearty manner, that it is a wonderful day to go sledding and what, for goodness sakes, are we waiting for? Let's all go! The whole darned family!

From that moment on, this citizen is worth watching.

It is discovered at once that he doesn't own any of the necessary clothing for an adventure of this kind. He must decide, therefore, whether he will go sledding in his new overcoat or resort to the old coachman's livery that has been hanging in the attic ever since grandfather plunged on International Tintype and had to sell his victoria. This colorful garment is immediately pressed into service by the family who claim that appearances mean nothing when you go coasting, and who then break into gales of merry laughter when they see how silly he looks. This merriment quickly subsides when it is noticed that Daddy's enthusiasm is beginning to cool, and the family goes more soberly about the job of outfitting him for this wintertime lark, wrapping his throat in an old fascinator, stuffing his feet into a pair of six-buckle, seven-league galoshes, and pulling over his ears a red stocking cap with a gay, green tassel.

And let's quit this monkey-business of pretending I'm talking about somebody else. How do I look?

Thus attired, I am led joyously from the house, handed a sled rope, and before you know it I am plodding down the middle of the street pulling the entire family. Dogs bark at me, neighbor children dance about me, laughing faces appear at windows, and an old man stops to eye the procession and cackles, "Durndest sight I seen since the St. Louie Exposition!"

It is a country mile to the coasting hill, someone having moved it recently, and since the only help I get from Mama, Sister, and Junior is an occasional "Giddap!" it is small wonder that, on arrival at the hill, I cry, "Now let's all go home, and this time you pull me!" But the family is not to be put off in this manner. This is where the fun begins, they point out. After all, what did we come here for?

What indeed?

It turns out that this hill is styled after the Matterhorn except that it is higher and steeper, and when this is observed it is decided, by majority rather than unanimous vote, that Daddy will have to guide and that the best way for him to do this is to lie down on his stomach—but why mince words!—the best way for him to do this is to go down belly-smacker with assorted members of the family riding on his back. This decision is reached without regard for the fact that Daddy has not gone belly-smacker since the Big Freeze of 1916 and that he has spent some of the best years of his life developing one of those soft undersides that Mr. Churchill used to talk about.

Meanwhile, other coasters have gathered about to admire my costume and to inquire whether I have lost my whip and to determine whether this quaint specimen is going to coast or is advertising something. This audience inspires me with a sort of crazy bravado, so I gingerly spread myself on the sled, Junior leaps on my back with a glad cry, and I am shortly going down the hill at eighty-three miles an hour, taking bumps that would pound the hull off a PT boat, whizzing past trees and boulders which I miss because I have had a blameless life and not because I have my eyes open, and shouting "Ooof!—Ugg!—Woosh!" and other remarks generally indicative of the fun I am having. The ride ends without permanent disaster surprisingly enough, and after about fifteen minutes of steady climbing I am back at the top of the hill where another relative is jumping up and down yelling, "My turn! My turn, Daddy! Let's go!" and we are off again with Daddy on the bottom feeling very much like an old pinball.

How long this went on I don't very well remember, but I do recall stumbling off about dark and hiding in a snowdrift. The family dug me out some minutes later, and they claim I was alternately paging a St. Bernard and crying, "Believe it or not, I am merely waiting for an avalanche."

That gave them something to laugh about all the way home. "Giddap, Daddy!" they would cry, and then they'd laugh and laugh.

But look how I've wandered from the subject! All I really wanted to say is that there comes a day in every man's life when he begins to look silly in a stocking cap.

Hold That Mower, Elmer

WELL, HERE we are at the time of year again when men who have no natural talent for it, and no experience either, get out their lawn mowers and make fools of themselves. To an expert—to one who has mowed the equivalent of Texas in his time—to me, in brief, there is nothing more ridiculous than the sight of a man who would not think of cutting his own hair, which is simple by comparison, panting about in pursuit of a lawn mower.

Perhaps I am sensitive on the subject, a weakness that probably goes back to the eight summers I worked for a landscape gardener and mowed slightly over four acres of lawn every week. That is a total of roughly four hundred acres or, if looked at lengthwise which is the way you push a lawn mower, is a swath two feet wide and one thousand eight hundred miles long, this being about the distance from Memphis to Los Angeles or from Hong Kong to Vladivostok. I prefer the Hong Kong to Vladivostok run myself. Seems more scenic, somehow, and you don't have to cross Arkansas. The point is, however, that when it comes to mowing lawns I will not take a back seat for anybody.

To begin with, no one should attempt to mow grass until he has thoroughly mastered the mechanics of the lawn mower. There is no reason why anyone should balk at this because the principle is relatively simple. Once you understand that it is more than happy coincidence that the wheels and the blades go around simultaneously, then you are on the right track. And once you understand that it is the action of the whirling blades which pulls the grass against the cutting edge, you are making progress. And when it finally dawns on you that there are boys who will set this whole process in motion and keep it going for as little as twenty-five cents an hour, then you are really getting someplace.

Perhaps you have noticed, however, that it is possible to push a lawn mower and still not cut any grass. In that event, one of two things has happened—either the blades are not working properly or you are pushing the thing upsidedown. A little adjustment of the blades requires only the twisting of four set-screws and you will know that they are set tight enough when it is impossible to push the machine in any direction.

So much for the engineering principles. The machine is all oiled, the blades are set, we have on our old pants, and we have spit on our hands. Where do we begin? Well, we can start on the sidewalk and take a few brisk turns around the block. This is recommended for beginners because there is nothing easier to mow than a sidewalk and this inspires confidence. Hardier householders, however, usually start on the lawn at once, promptly run into a rock, pitch forward on their faces and call it a day.

Generally speaking there are two kinds of lawns. One is the kind filled with rocks brought down by the glacier, the other is the kind filled with rocks brought down by those little people known as the neighbors' children. Often these rocks are invisible to the naked eye but the lawn mower that cannot find them is not worth the name and should be sent back to the factory for reconditioning. The same can be said of lawn mowers that cannot find wire, bottles, hoe handles, gum boots, and the old tire pump you thought you threw away last fall.

Very well. We are now well started and the question naturally arises whether to mow around the garbage can or lift it away while you mow where it was. When weighing this decision remember that it is only a matter of time until you will some day lift the can and the bottom will fall out of it. This consideration plus the natural desire of a proficient mower to do it the fancy way, may encourage you to mow around it. For somewhat different reasons it is also best to mow around trees, sundials and other stationary objects, but I certainly do not hold with a party of my acquaintance who carefully mowed around a tricycle.

Perhaps the best test of skill, and the one requiring the shrewdest judgment on the part of the operator, is mowing the terrace. Will he go up and down it, which is easy in one direction, or will he risk the sideways treatment which is not easy at any time but looks quicker? This is a purely rhetorical question to which there is no answer.

We now come to the flower beds. Not if we're lucky, of course, but the chances are that we now come to the flower beds and we might as well face it. The problem here is two-fold unless there are two flower beds whereupon it automatically becomes four-fold and new odds are posted. Will you sort of thrust the machine at the side of the bed, a

technique which, unless thoroughly mastered, will plunge you clear across it, leaving a lot of sadder but wiser petunias in your wake? Or will you try to hold one wheel in the air over the bed while you push the other on the ground, thus doing things to your spine that could conceivably send a chiropractor's son through Princeton? One does not lightly give advice on this point. I can only say that when I am done mowing there are plenty of cut flowers for ailing neighbors.

When you get right down to it there is nothing to mowing a lawn that a little patience won't solve. A little patience, a little practice, a little oil, and, as I have pointed out, a little boy to do it for you while you sit on the porch with your shoes off browsing through a Tom Collins.

Now then, is there any arnica in the house?

Mr. Stirpes, and My Lawful Living Issue

I HAVE JUST spent a cozy evening curled up with a brand new insurance policy and I am anxious to set down my impressions of this document provided I can see through these spots that are dancing before my eyes. Actually I could write a pretty colorful piece about the spots themselves which are about the size of manhole covers and are all red and green and gold and shoot off the gayest sparks. Spots before the eyes are no novelty to me, of course, now that the subject has come up. Indeed, I am considered an authority on them and you can believe me, therefore, when I say that the spots I am now seeing as a result of reading this insurance policy are by all odds the gaudiest variety observed in this section since a farmer of my acquaintance backed into an electric fence. He speaks very highly of the spots he saw on that occasion, which he well may do since he was alone and no one else saw them. However, I will not discredit him by saying that these I am now seeing are in any way superior, but I will say this: They are beauties. If you doubt it, get out one of your own policies and read all of the fine print.

It seems to me that an insurance policy could be a simple, forthright document. Its purpose is merely to record the fact that the proprietors of some insurance company with a name so long that it takes five minutes to pass a given point, have laid a bet that you are not going to be gathered to your reward before they have gathered theirs. To be sure, some reprehensible customers do die off schedule now and again, thus throwing the company for a loss, but by and large the company has the situation pretty well cased and stands to show a snug profit on the deal.

Now the details of this wager could be described in words of one syllable, and not too many of them either, but this is not done in any insurance policy I have ever seen. Do not use a short word where a long one will do, and do not use a long word where Latin will serve—that is the advice given to the authors who, having drifted from bad to worse, end up writing insurance policies.

By way of example, I am going to quote a paragraph from the rich prose devoted to an item called the "Settlement Agreement." I want you to read this quotation carefully so that you will know what I am talking about and because there is also a chance that you will see one or two attractive spots yourself. It reads,

> "Upon the death of the survivor of the insured and the above named beneficiary any funds then retained by the company shall be paid forthwith in equal shares to such of the children born of the marriage of the insured and the said wife as may then be living, and to the living lawful issue, per *Stirpes,* of such of said children as may then be deceased, but if none of said children, nor any of their lawful issue, shall then be living, then to be paid to the executors or administrators of the insured."

I take it to be the purpose of that paragraph to describe who is going to get the money when I have gone to the Happy Hunting Ground but, while I have read it both forwards and backwards, I still do not know who is going to collect. It looks a little as though somebody named Stirpes is going to get it, but since I am not acquainted with any Stirpes this does not clarify the matter. As for those "said children with their lawful issues"—can it be that it is the purpose of this policy to reward kids who are in the newspaper business? It is a novel idea and perhaps a good one, but frankly it is not at all what I had in mind.

In fact, I do not find anything that I had in mind contained in this policy. The agent who sold it to me talked about security, and assured educational opportunities, and a serene old age—all first-class stuff—but the policy does not mention anything about me fishing in Florida or facing life with a confident smile at age sixty. Instead it is full of things I never dreamed of and which I simply do not understand. Look! I can close my eyes and poke my finger anywhere and come up with a clause like this:

"If no such election is operative at the time of the death of the insured, the beneficiary entitled to receive the proceeds, if a natural person taking in his or her own right, may, with the consent of the company, exercise such right of election."

Perhaps this is not such a good example because the meaning of this section seems clear enough. It means that the policy is void unless there is an election—presidential, probably—and, not only that, it is void unless I am survived by a natural person. At this point we will pause while better odds are posted in favor of the insurance company. I might be able to arrange that election business if I put my mind to it, having tentatively selected the election of 1996, but who can say whether I will be survived by a natural person and, most particularly, by "a natural person taking in his or her own right." I do not know what that means exactly, but it does not sound like anybody I know.

In fact, it is this "natural person," or beneficiary, that I am thinking of as I protest the nature of this document. We Kirchers are just common folks. True, we are honest, hard-working, and friendly when treated well, but there has always been a wild strain of illiteracy in us. Some day, in the gloomy course of events, some Kirchers of this character will come upon this document. Being of a curious turn, they will examine it carefully, passing it among themselves, looking at it from all angles and holding it up to mirrors to see if it makes any better sense that way. They will then say, "He was well-meaning and all, but he kept some of the durndest trash." They will then throw the policy into the fireplace together with my pressed flowers and my collection of World's Fair picture postcards.

A few days later there will be a meeting in a distant city attended by six or eight plump, pleased men. They will be the officials of my insurance company brought together for the purpose of cutting another melon.

Bad cess to you, gentlemen!

Shame on All You Bankers!

IT MAY BE July when you read this. Or April. Or September. But it is early in January when I am writing it, and my head is as clear as a bell bong! bong! though frankly it wasn't much of a party. Just a few old, old friends—Old Granddad, Old Taylor, and Old Forrester to name a few.

In any case, this is the time of the year when you carefully open one eye to look at the newspapers and discover that financial institutions of one kind and another have purchased large advertisements to present what are variously called "Financial Statements," "Statements of Condition," "Comparative Financial Statements," and so forth, also known in some quarters as etcetera. By whatever names they are called, however, these announcements are all subject to the same weakness, or what appears to be a weakness to me.

To be sure, bankers have a right to look scornfully down their thin noses when I waltz in bearing criticism, because all I know about banking could be placed in a small safe deposit box with enough room left over for a dressed rabbit. On the other hand, these "Financial Statements" seem to be directed to the public, and I am a member of the public in good standing, so if I do not understand them and choose to say so, then the bankers had best sit quietly in the dugout until it is their turn to come to bat.

After all, this is a democracy, wasn't it?

The outstanding curiosity to be noted in a "Financial Statement" lies in the fact that the Liabilities always equal the Assets. On your left are the Assets, a very neat column of them which, when it is totaled, is found to amount to $9,543,617.19. And there, on your right, are the Liabilities, listed as disarmingly as any one could ask, and when they are totaled it is found—guess what!—that they also equal $9,543,617.19!

You go around laughing at miracles, but how else are you going to account for a thing like that?

Even granting that the liabilities are supposed to equal assets—which I refuse to do—isn't it more than mortal man can swallow to believe that they will come out to the penny like that? Financial institutions are big places. They employ hundreds of people, many of them human. For a whole year all these people take in money and give out money and make change and run accounting machines and goodness knows what else, and nobody ever drops a nickel through a crack in the floor, nobody ever mislays a decimal point, and nobody ever adds six to seven and gets twelve! Isn't that the classiest and most staggering performance that a mind can hope to grasp? And once you have grasped it, don't you feel like letting go of it again?

Mind you, I'm not reflecting on the character of bankers and you will please not go around saying that I am, but you can quote me to this effect if you like: the first financial institution that has the courage to admit that there is an unaccountable difference of six bits between its assets and its liabilities—that bank gets my business. I like people who make small mistakes and admit them.

We now come to the basic fatuity in the wobbly theory that liabilities should equal assets. As long as liabilities are allowed to roam around equalling assets then it does not seem to me that we are getting anywhere, as a look at my own case will prove. It was not my intention to publish a "Statement of Financial Condition" this year—it is such a ratty old thing—but if it will clear up this here basic fatuity I'm talking about, well for goodness sakes, let's do it. It follows:

STATEMENT OF FINANCIAL CONDITION

ASSETS:	
Cash on hand	$ 6.75
Cash hidden somewhere by my wife	13.65
War Stamps in book	32.25
Furniture and Fixtures	346.16
Bottle Deposits Accrued	1.15
Miscellaneous Assets	1.17
Total Assets	$401.13

LIABILITIES:	
Insurance	$ 43.16
Paper Boy	.47
Installments, One Kind & Another	116.35
Overdrawn at Bank (their figures)	51.18
Owed to Butcher	38.17
Owed to Baker	21.87
Owed to Candle-Stick Maker	129.93
Total Liabilities	$401.13

From those figures one great big ugly fact stands out. If I pay all my liabilities I will use up all my assets. In other words, I am just the same as dead broke right now. For me, this is not an unusual condition, but it should be remembered that I do not have a vault or a revolving door and that I am therefore no financial institution.

Financial institutions, it seems to me, would have more pride. At least they shouldn't brag about it in the papers.

For shame!

"Bye! Baby Bunting!"

NIMROD REPORTING, and here it is hunting season again, bang! bang!

Now really, fellows, is there anything better than a day in the field, the fall wind moist on your cheeks, the tawny countryside stretched ten miles and perhaps more before you, good rich earth clinging to your low-cuts, briars snatching at your pants, your trusty shooting iron growing three pounds heavier every minute, and the thrilling ever-present prospect of shooting a rabbit, a pheasant or another hunter! Could I look you in the eye and tell you there is anything better than that?

I hope to tell you I could!

Maybe when you get right down to it, I'm not a Nimrod at all. I've looked the word up in the dictionary and this is what it says:

> NIMROD—Biblical character, son of Cush, who was a mighty hunter and ruler.

I am confident that I am not a Biblical character and I am just as confident my father's name is not Cush. Doesn't sound familiar. To make sure, however, I phoned him. "Cush?" he replied. "Have you gone crazy?" As for being a mighty hunter, I don't seem to classify there either. To be sure I'd make a good ruler if anybody would ever listen to me, but that seems beside the point, so I have concluded that no fair-minded jury in the world would convict me of being Nimrod.

I believe my main trouble is that game is always scarce on the day I go hunting. On the day *before* I go hunting—say! you've never seen so much game in all your life—the air so full of pheasants that several hunters couldn't get their breath and were treated for asthma. And the day *after* I go hunting—brother, you listen to me!—couple fellows got caught in a rabbit stampede south of Waynesville and were nearly trampled to death. But these reports concern only those days when I'm doing something else. Let me sally into the woods, either alone or with somebody, preferably Sally, and the only game I see is an old Parchesi board forgotten by an absent-minded member of the Sunshine Society following a recent All Day Outing and Potato Salad Carnival. As for rabbits and pheasants, do you want to make me laugh, or would you rather step a little closer and let me beat you over the head with my gun butt?

It's the same way with fishing, too, just in case an editor of *Field and Stream* happens to be eavesdropping. The day before—wow! The day after—wow! But let me go off with rod and reel and the only fish reported in the entire world that day is a sperm whale off the Greenland coast, and *he* wasn't feeling well!

The weather now joins the conspiracy. All hunting days are fair and lovely, save one. All hunting days take years from the lives of hunters and return them to their pursuits invigorated and with an increased life expectancy—except one. On the day I go hunting the elements are holding tryouts for the next catastrophe, and so we are given exhibitions of lightning, thunder, driving rain, sleet, hail, snow, and high winds. Being unaccustomed to rigors of this kind, this poorly assorted weather generally gives me the ague and frequently my teeth chatter until after Christmas.

Still, I go hunting almost every year.

This means getting up before dawn, of course, because the hunting is never any good around here. That's another funny thing. The hunting is always good somewhere else—near Lima, for instance. So we get up early because we have to drive a long way and because we have to fight the traffic of Lima hunters who think the hunting is better down here. This, as I say, means getting up early, and it also means standing on the curb for an hour because the fellow-whose-alarm-didn't-go-off is standard equipment on any hunting trip. But at last the car pulls up to the curb and we're off for a regular day of it.

What a bluff, hearty crowd we are as we pile out of the car, our jackets smelling of moth balls, our hunting caps at rakish angles, our pockets swollen with shells, our guns carefully pointed in all directions. We take deep breaths of the sodden air and cry, "Ah!" meanwhile holding out our hands in the rain to prove it isn't raining. But who cares? It's over the fence and into the fields because today it's bound to be different and every thicket is full of—who's that?

What a bluff hearty crowd we are as we pile out of the car.

Oh, a farmer. "Good morning, sir. Fine morning. How's that? Signs? What signs? We didn't see any signs. Oh, the place is posted, eh? No hunting, eh? Well, well. Hey, fellows. The owner here says we can't hunt. Let's go."

So we quietly climb back over the fence feeling like—but I will not attempt to describe how we feel. We feel just like five grown men who have climbed over a fence and who have been confronted by one farmer and who are now climbing back over the fence while the farmer leans against a tree watching. It is that kind of a feeling—no other kind.

But that farmer doesn't get off so easy. Once we are in the car and have backed out of the lane, we discuss him. Who does he think he is? we ask. The Governor of the State? That's what's the matter with this country, no hospitality. If you ask us, the farmer's lot is not going to be improved until he learns better manners. Who does he think he is anyway? The Secretary of Agriculture? What was it we wanted to do anyway? Just walk across his infernal property, and maybe shoot a rabbit that is just as much ours as his. After all, we're taxpayers, aren't we? Who does he think he is anyway? The President of the United States? With talk as intemperate as this I certainly wouldn't want to be in that farmer's shoes.

But bad luck of this kind doesn't last forever and before long our little party, which has turned a rather attractive pastel blue by this time, is in the field again.

We fan out, of course. All hunters fan out. In this way we cover more territory and thus the brave tan line advances across the countryside—keen, alert, guns loaded and held in readiness for come what may. Tense as advancing infantrymen we prowl forward, passing other equally tense hunters who are prowling in the opposite direction. Silent as our pioneer forebears, except when we pause to blow our noses, we slowly traverse the length of a county or two and then swing back to the car, our jackets empty of game, but our shoes heavy with feet.

Night has fallen when the car pulls away from the curb and I shout a last good-by to those fine and fearless companions. As I stumble into the kitchen, the gunstock bumping along the floor behind me, my wife looks brightly eager and cries, "Howdy, Nimrod! Where's the moose?"

Women can be *so* unfeeling.

"*Grand Right and Left*"

EVERY NOW and then I go crazy and tell myself that civilization is at a standstill because we have deserted all the fine old customs of American life. House raisings, for instance. Back in pioneer days, everybody knocked off for miles around to help a neighbor clear his lot and build his cabin. Nothing of the sort can be done these days because all the neighbors I know either have houses or want new ones that are filled with plumbing, wiring and other complications. In addition, if word got around that a bunch of us were getting together for a house raising, representatives of the building trade unions would be on hand to dissuade us with hammers, wrenches, shovels, and other heavy tools of their crafts. So house raisings are probably impractical.

But we never have taffy pulls either, or apple-peeling parties at cider time. We never gather around the old upright, tilt back our mustaches, and sing, "In the Gloaming, Oh, My Darling!" and other fine old songs. What's more we never enjoy the clean and rousing fun of that wonderful American institution, the good old-fashioned square dance.

See? I said I was crazy.

And I can prove it, because about a week ago I was in the midst of one of these misty-eyed moods, softly sobbing about things I've never done, when out of a clear sky comes an invitation to go to a square dance and I leaped to my feet yelling, "Let's!" when what I should have said is, "You can take that fine old American institution and do-see-do the hell out of here. And stay out!"

(Incidentally, I have a note from my pastor saying it is all right to use profanity in a situation as aggravating as this.)

But when you have said that you will go to a square dance, and particularly when your partner has made herself a fetching dirndl for the occasion, then take it from Hiram it is only a matter of time until you find yourself sprawled in the corner of a barn counting your teeth.

That ain't dancing, kids, that's mayhem set to music!

At my age it is bad enough to cope with a single partner.

To understand square dancing you must remember that you have seven opponents in there with you, including your wife and six equally ruthless people. This considerably complicates matters for a man like me, who, when he can be persuaded to go dancing, customarily grabs the prettiest girl and foxtrots while everyone else is waltzing. At my age it is bad enough to cope with a single partner. I should stay out of such dances as "Dive for the Oyster" that begin when, in a voice that would make a foghorn wince, the caller yells, *"All join hands and circle west, Stride and strut and bust yore vest, and Swing that gal you love the best, Then promenade, oh promenade home!"*

Actually this man does not speak any plainer than a tobacco auctioneer with laryngitis, but he stands up there yammering these instructions about "busting yore vest," and before you know it you are caught in the awfulest maelstrom of hustling humanity, a swiftly swirling circle of swinging, prancing maniacs that rises to such a fury of speed and perspiration that you are apt to be flung from it by sheer centrifugal force, thus ending the dance from a ringside seat in a punch bowl.

My mistake, I reckon, was getting into a group—or "square" as it is called—who knew how to square dance and could read the caller's mind. Nobody seemed filled with confusion but me. No more was needed. I contained enough confusion for all eight of us, with enough left over to rattle the Sphinx.

"Ladies to the center and back to the bar, Gents go in and form a star," he yelled. I did it. I ran into the center to form a star, collided with a lady who was probably coming back to the bar, and formed a very nice constellation if I do say so myself. Still reeling from this attack of astronomy I heard the cry *"Allemande left!"* I didn't blame her. If Allemande left she was a smart girl. If I form one more star, I decided, he can yell, *"Kircher left, too!"*—but there wasn't time to reflect on this pleasant prospect because the lady at my left grabbed me, pulled me through a short hard circle and then, to the instruction *"Grand right and left!"* I found myself fighting all seven of them as I tried to claw my way around a circle that was going the other direction.

"The other way!" my partners yelled, and shoved me and pulled me and tripped me and then finally led me back to stand beside my wife, who by now was thinking darkly of divorce. "Is it over?" I gasped, but that was a foolish question.

"Meet yore honey and pass her by . . ."

"And a howdy-you-do, and a left hand back, and a how-are-you . . ."

"Put your little foot, put your little foot, put your little foot right there . . ."

"Gents swing out and ladies swing in, and form that Texas Star ag'in . . ."

Oh, it went on like that for hours, with me swinging in with the ladies instead of out with the gents, and do-see-do-ing with a six-foot farmer when I ought to be passing my honey by, and how-are-youing with the wrong hand when I should have been howdy-doing with my little foot right there, probably, and getting wonderfully disheveled, what with my shirt tail out, and falling down a good deal, and once nearly toppling backward out the window when an exceedingly hardy woman swung me around her head and let go.

But there! It is much too embarrassing to describe in any detail. It is enough to say that I had a bad time of it. And then let us merely add that I have revised my opinions about fine old American customs, and that there is one fine old American custom in particular that knows where it can go. Indeed, it does. I gave it colorful directions several times that night.

Hot and Cold Running Anguish

IT ISN'T my intention to suggest that we are any better than anybody else when I say that we Kirchers have always been great ones for taking baths. This habit goes back for many generations and I can produce documents to prove that the reason Caleb Kircher did not sign the Declaration of Independence is because he claimed to feel sticky and went home to take a bath. Thus, through the years, people have been making kidding remarks: "You can't call the Kirchers honest, but they certainly are kempt," and "A disorderly crowd, to be sure, but tidy," and "A passel of rascals, admitted, but give them credit, they're sanitary."

Naturally, I am proud of this fine old family tradition and naturally, too, I cherish the memories of many an excellent bath. Not wishing to be indelicate I will not describe in any detail how, during my youth on a farm, I bathed in a simple washtub placed by the stove in the kitchen and filled with water carried from the neighbor's pump. I will refrain from saying, "Ah! Those Were the Good Old Days!" because, "Ah! They Weren't!"

And I will not tell you how all through the warm months we would bathe in the ole swimmin' hole or, as I laughingly called it, the old drownin' hole, because I couldn't swim. Darned if I'm even going to tell you how, on my return to plumbing, I learned to love real porcelain bathtubs and how I would languish in them when I should have been playing shortstop. It seems to me that all of that is none of your business. How would *you* like someone prying into *your* bathing record, provided you have one?

The only point I care to make, now that the subject has come up, is simply that this tradition for cleanliness had just about come to the end of the line, the victim of a modern convenience—the shower bath.

I blush to admit it (and it's time some blushing was done in this piece!) but I never had much experience with showers until a couple of years ago. At that time we moved into a house that has many modern innovations (for instance, there's a machine in the kitchen that makes real ice! You heard me! Real ice!) and among them is a shower bath that was so eloquently praised by the former tenant that I half expected it to squirt strawberry sodas.

It doesn't, however. It squirts water—the most unreliable water, the most unpredictable water, the most inclement water, the most contrary, mule-headed, prejudiced, bigoted water; water that alternately turns you blue and scarlet; water that would disgrace a cloudburst and cause tornadoes, typhoons and tidal waves to seek more respectable company.

(Somewhere along about here we may as well pause to rebuke the plumbing-fixture people. For years they have been selling showers by showing pictures of pretty girls not very well concealed behind shower curtains. There are four or five men in the country—of whom I am in no wise one—who will ignore such a picture. The rest of us will stop to

I half expected it to squirt strawberry sodas.

admire this girl and to wonder whether some good correspondence school offers a course in advertising photography. Failing to reflect that it is a shower and not a girl we are buying, we are so taken with her daintiness, freshness, and charm that we eventually phone a plumber and the rest is history, up to its old trick of repeating itself. A snake tells Eve to offer Adam an apple. The Amalgamated Shower-Bath Manufacturers pay a girl to dress like Eve and offer him a bathtub. It is high time that I, and the rest of us Adams, get next to the fact that a woman's wiles are often in the employ of somebody who wants us to guess which shell the pea is under.)

But to get back to my own shower. It has two faucets, one labeled "Hot" and the other labeled "Cold," both cruel understatements. It is the problem once you have disrobed—don't stare please!—to twist these two handles so that a mixture of comfortably warm water is produced. This requires the touch of a surgeon because, once the shower has unburdened itself of several snorts of brown scalding water, it settles down to producing either boiling water or ice water. The most delicate twisting of the knobs is required to bring the water to a safe temperature, after which you are permitted to cross your fingers and step under the cleansing stream.

From here on it would be simple were it not for the fact that the shower is hooked into the general plumbing system. Thus, every time a faucet elsewhere in the house is turned on, the water under which you are standing is violently affected.

If Mother, for instance, draws a pan of hot water for the dishes, you are instantly deluged with water that would freeze a pelican. Gasping for breath you dash—wet, nude and soapy—to the head of the stairs and scream to the effect that you are taking a shower for heaven's sakes and do not monkey with the faucets. This earns you the kind of glum silence that needs no translation. But the faucet is turned off and you return to the shower, adjust the water again and start over.

Then Junior decides to sprinkle the lawn. There is every reason why he shouldn't do this. The lawn doesn't need sprinkling. As a general thing he doesn't like to sprinkle the lawn. He is supposed to be at the playground practicing basketball. But something draws him home, something lures him to the faucet, something overcomes his normal distaste for sprinkling, and he begins to sprinkle. In another fraction of a second you are the howling victim of second-degree burns. And this time you

Gasping for breath, you dash to the head of the stairs.

are heard throughout the neighborhood as you inquire whether the family wishes you to perish. You want to know whether you have lived a blameless life just to be boiled in a bathtub. You want to know whether all families are so depraved, so wanting in common compassion, that they will conspire to torment a parent who would not, for his part, harm a hair on their silly heads. As I have said, these pertinent questions are put in a loud voice and they generally cause Junior to turn off the hose with the morose announcement that he can't do nothing around here no more.

Back to the shower until Sister—but must we go into that? She only wanted a drink of water. She was thirsty, and all she wanted was a little old drink of water. After all, everybody wants a drink of water now and then, and it is coming to a pretty pass when a body can't do the dishes or sprinkle the lawn or get a drink just because some thin-skinned old grouch is taking a shower. We are all screaming by this time, and what I am screaming is that I will never take another shower so long as I so-help-me live, and family tradition or no family tradition, I would rather be dirty than dead.

Sometimes things don't calm down until the following day.

Set in Baskerville and Bulmer types
Format by D. F. Bradley
Lithographed by the Murray Printing Company, Inc.
Bound by The Haddon Craftsmen, Inc.
Published by HARPER & BROTHERS, *New York*

DATE DU
GAYLORD
PRINTED IN U.S.A.